OUR INDUSTRIAL PAST

MORE OF BRITAIN'S INDUSTRIAL HERITAGE

written and photographed by
JOHN HANNAVY

First published in Great Britain in 2016

Every attempt has been made by the author and publisher to secure the appropriate permissions for materials reproduced in this book. If there has been any oversight we will be happy to rectify the situation and a written submission should be made to the Publishers.

A CIP catalogue record for this book is available from the British Library.

ISBN 978 0 85710 100 6

PiXZ Books
Halsgrove House, Ryelands Business Park, Bagley Road, Wellington, Somerset TA21 9PZ
Tel: 01823 653777
Fax: 01823 216796
email: sales@halsgrove.com

An imprint of Halstar Ltd, part of the Halsgrove group of companies
Information on all Halsgrove titles is available at: www.halsgrove.com

Printed and bound in China by Everbest Printing Investment Ltd

Front cover image: Hereford Waterworks' triple-expansion pumping engine – seen here in steam – was built by Worth, Mackenzie & Co at their Phoenix Engine Works in Stockton-on-Tees in 1895. This massive engine is the oldest triple-expansion, double-acting, inverted, condensing steam engine still operating in the UK.

Title page image: Net lofts and fishing boats on the shingle beach at Hastings.

Contents page image: The author in the cockpit of a Tornado jet at Boscombe Down. "Don't touch the lever between your legs" said the technician, "the ejector seat is fully armed and we'd hate to have to scrape you off the hanger roof."

My thanks go to the many museum curators throughout the country who have granted me access to their collections and offered valuable advice. Thanks also to Chris Hall for his technical input on early tanks, and, as ever, to my wife Kath, for her enduring tolerance and support.

By the same author:
Britain's Industrial Heritage
Edwardian Mining In Old Postcards
The Once-Ubiquitous Paddle Steamer
Preserved Steam-Powered Machines

CONTENTS

INTRODUCTION

ONE OF THE ENDURING DELIGHTS of Britain's architectural and industrial heritage is that, no matter how long you spend trying, you will never see more than a small fraction of it all. That is what keeps us exploring. It is also what drives armies of enthusiastic volunteers – and a growing number of specialist professional conservators and restorers – to preserve and provide access to that heritage.

Like my earlier book – *Britain's Industrial Heritage* – to which this is a companion volume, a thematic approach has been used to explore the rich legacy of past generations.

This latest compendium draws on my experiences exploring an eclectic range of heritage sites, from vast steam engines to tiny candlemakers' workshops, from brickmakers to gunsmiths, and from fishing fleets to gasworks and power-stations.

In keeping with the pattern established in my earlier books, and where they amplify or contextualise the story, my own images are complemented by photographs from my Victorian and Edwardian collection. Edwardian postcards, especially, give us an insight into which aspects of life and heritage were of interest a century ago.

above: The elaborate label on the door of a Victorian safe, now preserved in Barrington Court, Somerset.

opposite page: The wooden-clad cylinders of the great steam engines at Eastney Pumpng Station in Hampshire.

left: In the recreation of Thomas Trevor's Victorian candle-maker's workshop – part of the Blists Hill Victorian Town in Shropshire and originally sited in nearby Telford – visitors can see candles being made by what was then considered to be mass production. Many of the candles produced in the works would have been used underground in the nearby coal mines.

right: A close-up view of a steel rolling mill on display at Kelham Island Museum in Sheffield. Lengths of red-hot steel were progressively passed between the pair of rollers from left to right, getting narrower and narrower until the required profile was achieved.

below: A steam hammer built by Charles Ross of Sheffield, also on display at Kelham. Lights are cleverly used to create the appearance of a red-hot bar of metal being pounded into shape.

Discovering both the architectural and industrial reminders of Britain's past – and usually armed with my camera – has occupied a large proportion of my adult life.

Exploring industrial sites such as New Lanark, and Manchester's Liverpool Road Station – the world's first passenger railway terminus – before they were ever even considered as candidates for rescue and restoration, were my early introductions.

Recent years have seen a considerable number of long-term restoration projects come to fruition, contributing so much to the range of visitor experiences on offer – and significantly adding to the impossibility of visiting them all.

Some others, like the Wigan Pier project which recreated life and work in the Lancashire town around 1900, have closed their doors – a result of under-investment in keeping the experience fresh and engaging for a new generation of visitors.

Less than a century ago, history was accessed from books and visits to rather staid museums. The heritage culture was still decades in the future, and while the wealthy did visit the great architectural remains of past civilisations on their Grand Tours, the idea of visiting a

left: *Nora*, an 0-4-
0ST steam engine,
built in 1920 by
Andrew Barclay &
Son at Kilmarnock
for the Blaenavon
Company, with Works
No.1680, stands on
static display below
the headframe of
the Big Pit at
Blaenavon in South
Wales.

below: The giant
steam engine at
Wigan's
Trencherfield Mill —
the largest mill
engine in the world
still operational in
its original engine
house — is steamed
regularly for visitors.
Originally fuelled by
local Wigan coal, it
is now steamed using
biofuel.

century-old mill steam engine would have seemed to them quite alien – and in any case, it would still be have been being used for its original purpose, powering the mill.

Reading tourist books from the early years of the last century, the differences between leisure activities then – for those who had leisure time – and now is quite different. Even the great medieval abbeys and castles so popular today were seldom visited by the majority of people.

Writers – including H. V. Morton whose accounts of his travels in Britain in the 1920s were hugely popular both in his best-selling books and his newspaper columns – did visit shipyards, silk mills, potteries, steel works and so on, and write about them, but they were all working enterprises, rather than staged resurrections.

Even the idea of 'industrial heritage' as a concept – let alone as a subject for academic study and research as it is today – or as a major leisure activity, is still a relatively recent one.

Until the mid 1930s, the idea of preserving obsolete industrial sites and artefacts had never even been considered, so the heritage movement is little more than eighty years old.

right: The Levant Mine from a 1905 tinted postcard, one of an extensive series of cards depicting the Cornish mining landscape, and the life and work of the miners.

It was in 1935 that the Cornish Engines Preservation Committee was formed to rescue the Levant winding engine, between Pendeen and St Just in Cornwall, which was scheduled to be demolished and scrapped.

Just thirty years before the committee to save the Levant beam engine was set up, the working mine had been celebrated in a series of postcards, but by 1930, with its seams of tin and copper too difficult and expensive to extract, the operation had been closed.

Now in the care of the National Trust, the Levant engine is the only surviving Cornish Beam Engine in the world, still driven by steam in its original engine house. It is regularly steamed for visitors. The surviving buildings are now part of

right: The iconic view of the Forth Railway Bridge, one of only two structures on the list of British World Heritage Sites still performing its original function. If some enterprising entrepreneurs started regular steam-hauled vintage train services over the under-used bridge, they could have a significant tourist attraction on their hands.

left: Part of
Liverpool's historic
waterfront, including
the 'Three Graces' –
The Royal Liver
Building, The Cunard
Building and the Port
of Liverpool Building
– seen from the
deck of the
Birkenhead ferry.
To the right is the
strikingly modern
Museum of Liverpool.

the Cornwall and West Devon Mining World Heritage Site, one of twenty-six World Heritage Sites in the United Kingdom.

The formation of the Cornish Engines Preservation Committee in 1935 is generally accepted as marking the beginning of the whole heritage preservation movement which today has spawned hundreds of preservation societies and industrial trusts, responsible for the preservation, restoration and management of well over one thousand sites across the country which, had they been lost, would have left an irreparable hole in the industrial history of Britain.

The movement got off to a slow start, however, as the Second World War, followed by years of austerity, put many embryonic projects on hold. It was the late 1950s before things got going again.

It is a significant measure of just how successful the industrial heritage movement has been in just eighty years, that nine of the World Heritage Sites in the United Kingdom are industrial – the other eight being The Forth Rail Bridge (added to the list in 2015), Blaenavon (2000), Derwent Valley Mills (2001), Ironbridge Gorge (1986), Liverpool's Maritime Waterfront (2004), New Lanark (2001), the Pontcysllte Viaduct and Ellesmere Canal (2009), and Saltaire Mill and Model Village (2001). The Cornwall and West Devon sites were added in 2006.

There is also a further 'tentative' list of sites aspiring for World Heritage status, and that includes Chatham's Historic Naval Dockyard and the Jodrell Bank Radio Telescope – by far the most modern on the list – and the survivals of North Wales's extensive slate industry.

below: Work began on restoring Liverpool's Albert and Canning Docks in the 1970s. This view dates from the early 1980s. Jesse Hartley's unique Albert Dock warehouses now house shops, bars, the Tate Northern and the Merseyside Maritime Museum.

Many of today's heritage sites contain artifacts brought together from several locations, the host sites seeking to present visitors with a more complete picture than might otherwise have been possible. Some, like the Victorian industrial towns at Blists Hill and Beamish, were created on sites which already had the surviving remains of a range of industrial activities, and hugely engaging as they are, they have, unavoidably, a sort of artificiality about them – not always a bad thing, as long as they are approached as such.

There is always an inherent risk in accessing history in the manner we do today – a risk that the harsh realities of Victorian and Edwardian life have to be sanitised and dumbed down to the extent that they become more like period theme parks than genuine survivals of a bygone world.

Striking the happy balance between those two quite different things is never easy, and many books and articles have been written about the dangers of over-stepping what is, after all, a quite arbitrary line. Curators face a massive on-going challenge in getting the balance right, refreshing the ways in which the stories of the sites in their care are communicated, while still attracting audiences who are increasingly more used to accessing their history through touch-screen computer tablets and televised drama documentaries

Many of the industries which are represented on our heritage map today were highly dangerous, and operated with little regard for employee safety. Injuries and deaths abounded. Thus, the conflicting demands of safety and accessibility have to be met in a manner which is both sensible and practical.

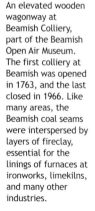

An elevated wooden wagonway at Beamish Colliery, part of the Beamish Open Air Museum. The first colliery at Beamish was opened in 1763, and the last closed in 1966. Like many areas, the Beamish coal seams were interspersed by layers of fireclay, essential for the linings of furnaces at ironworks, limekilns, and many other industries.

However obtrusive they may be for those of us with cameras, protective barriers are no more than simple common sense, especially when children are admitted to engine houses, mills and the like – even though children historically worked there in appalling conditions and were the most frequently maimed and injured.

Many industrial attractions get the balance about right, but a few do not. If their primary purpose is simply to educate – as was so often the case as recently as my own childhood – the visitor experience might prove unappealing. If the primary purpose is to do no more than entertain, then while the commercial viability of the project may be sustainable, one of the early casualties will doubtless be historical accuracy, simply in order to put on an attractive show.

Where re-enactment is part of the experience, what we see should pretty much always be taken with a healthy pinch of salt, simply because that re-enactment – be it a snapshot of life from the 18th, 19th or 20th century – will be 'performed' subject to the sometimes over-protective requirements of current health and safety legislation, the terms and conditions of carefully-worded insurance policies, and a whole raft of other constraints which never bothered the workers whose lives and experiences are being re-enacted.

Having said that, the number of heritage sites open to visitors is at an all-time high, and increasing annually – as are the numbers of us visiting them. Without the vision and perseverance of experts, enthusiasts and volunteers over the past eighty years, our understanding of life in Britain's industrial heyday would be much less complete.

John Hannavy 2016

Apart from the passengers' clothing, this recreates a scene which would have been typical on many streets more than eighty years ago as the drivers of former Sunderland tram No.16 (built 1900) and the single-deck Gateshead No.10 (built mid-1920s) have a chat at one of the tram stops at Beamish Open Air Museum.

BUILDING BRITAIN

IN THE STONEMASONS' YARD at Salisbury Cathedral, a group of dedicated craftsmen – and craftswomen – work year-round renewing the decaying stonework of the 800-year-old building. They use the same skills – and many of the same tools – as the men who originally built it. The necessary concessions to modern health and safety requirements, and the occasional use of power tools to roughly shape the stones before the fine carving work begins, are the most obvious differences.

Work on this latest restoration started in 1986 and should be complete by 2018, so the renewal project will have taken thirty-two years – only six fewer than it took to build the cathedral in the first place. "The work we are doing today," said Head Mason Chris Sampson in 2010 "is the best that has ever been done on the building – and much better than the original masons achieved in the 13th century." Watching his skilled masons at work, that is not hard to believe.

Given that the cathedral, apart from its slightly later spire, was built from start to finish in less than forty years – the working lifetime of two generations in the 13th century – the pace of construction must have been considerable.

Sampson painted a picture of jobbing masons, paid on lowly piece-work rates, working flat out to get the job done, and perhaps paying less attention to the fine detail on stones which would be positioned a hundred feet or more above ground level. If it looked good from the ground, then in medieval terms it was acceptable.

opposite page: Alan Spittle, one of the stonemasons at work in the yard at Salisbury Cathedral in 2010. He is part of a dedicated team of 21st century craftsmen and women working continuously on the fabric of the building – the latest phase of the renewal process which has taken place on the church throughout the centuries. Many cathedrals now have their own apprentice-training schemes, to ensure that they maintain a pool of talented men and women with the skills they need. Much of their work involves rectifying Victorian and Edwardian errors.

inset: From a century earlier, a stonemason's yard in Nottingham, c.1910.

left: Stonemasons at work in an Aberdeen granite works, from a tinted postcard published c.1905.

this page: All aspects of Edwardian industry were featured on postcards, and these cards illustrate just three of the many stone quarries to be found around Britain. While the location of the quarry in the top card is unknown, the Cheese Wring Quarry near Liskeard, middle, was the scene of an early campaign by environmentalists as the beautiful Cheese Wring rocks nearby were in danger of collapse due to blasting in the quarries. Part of Portland Quarry, bottom, was worked by convicts from the nearby prison.

opposite top left: Portland Quarry today, with a rusting hoist — perhaps one of those in the postcard — and beyond, cut blocks of stone.

top right: The unassuming entrance to Beer Quarry Caves — seen here on a cold Easter weekend — gives no clue to the magical journey underground which awaits visitors.

bottom: Exeter Cathedral was one of the many cathedrals built of stone from Beer.

The building of great cathedrals required access to large quarries of high quality stone – and the remains of those quarries can be seen all over the countryside. Some are today little more than scars on a hillside, but others are much more engaging, none more so, perhaps, than the Beer Quarry Caves in Devon. Beer Caves, a network of underground caverns, have been systematically excavated for nearly two thousand years for their fine Beer Freestone – a chalk limestone laid down between 65 and 140 million years ago.

Soft when cut – and therefore easy to work – Beer stone can be found in at least twenty-four cathedrals including Exeter, Winchester and St Paul's.

The Romans were the first to quarry the stone, with later generations moving the working face deeper and deeper underground – so despite the age of the workings, walking through the caves is actually a journey forward in time, starting with the Romans and moving through the centuries until the quarry closed in 1920.

right: Digging clay at Bursledon, Hampshire, late 1890s. The clay continued to be dug by hand well into the 1930s. By the time the workings finally closed in the 1970s, the clay was being cut more than a mile from the brickworks and transported from the claypit by conveyor belt, narrow-gauge railway and overhead aerial ropeway.

above: A collection of moulds for hand-made bricks, stored at Bursledon Brickworks. Some of these date back to the early years of the 20th century.

right: A 1/6th plate ambrotype – glass positive – photograph from the 1860s showing a team of workers making bricks by hand in the Manchester area, photographer unknown.

A new quarry was opened at that time, and stone was cut from there for eighty years – much of it used to replace eroded stonework on medieval cathedrals and churches – until that, too, closed in 2003. In 2013, it was re-opened so that the restorers of Exeter Cathedral could extract Beer stone once again as the cathedral's refurbishment continues over the next ten years.

More than seven hundred years after the majority of the medieval cathedrals were built, another great new cathedral was consecrated – but it was not built of local stone hand-cut

by a team of stone masons. The Cathedral of the Holy Spirit in Guildford, Surrey, was entirely constructed using that most uniquitous of building materials – red brick.

The story of the humble brick is a fascinating one – a story of an established technology which was lost for almost a thousand years after the Romans left Britain in the early years of the 5th century.

When brick-making was re-introduced in the 15th century, it became a material used for only the finest buildings – bricks being hand-made and expensive – before becoming the ubiquitous building material it is today once mass-production had been introduced.

In the early 19th century, many small estates, towns and villages all had their own brickworks, usually simply supplying local needs.

Brickmaking was, at that time, largely seasonal – restricted to the warmer months of the year as the bricks had to be slowly dried before they could be fired in simple kilns. If the water content of the bricks was too high before they were fired, they would explode in the kilns as the water rapidly vapourised within the clay.

One such brickworks, at Charlestown on the Firth of Forth, had been established in the 1780s to exploit a local clay which was, in part, a by-product of the mining industry. The village was surrounded by extensive deposits of coal and limestone, but access to both these important commodities required the removal of large quantities of fireclay.

As the Earl of Elgin's huge limekilns were already in production – with a constant demand for firebricks – that clay

above left: Tattershall Castle in Lincolnshire, built between 1434 and 1447 by Ralph Cromwell, the Lord Treasurer of England, was one of Britain's earliest major brick buildings. Constructing the six-storey castle of brick was a clear statement of both wealth and power.

above: Doves pecking at a brick wall in the gardens of Felbrigg Hall in Norfolk. It is believed that the attraction is the lime mortar used in the construction of the 17th century wall. By the 1620s when the hall itself was being enlarged, brick was considered to be the height of fashion, and an ornate brick facade was constructed, concealing the earlier Tudor manor-house.

above: Making bricks by hand, 1890s — one half of a stereoscopic (3D) photograph.

above right: The remains of the Earl of Elgin's huge limekilns at Charlestown on the Firth of Forth. The kilns were re-lined at least once per year with bricks made from local fireclay and manufactured at the nearby estate-owned brickworks.

right: From the 1845 wages book of the Charlestown Brick & Tile Works, it seems that some men were on day rates, most on piece work. In an advertisement dated 1840, the company announced that "This Establishment is now in full operation and have for sale Common Bricks of every description" as well as fire bricks, roof tiles, drainpipes, clay water pipes, chimney pots, and a range of other clayware. The works had been in operation since the 1780s.

left: William Longley of Leeds patented his brick-making machine in 1863 which, he claimed, produced pressure-moulded bricks from wet clay with greater solidity, a smoother outer surface, and a lower moisture content than those which could be manufactured either by hand or by using any of the other machines then available. The journal, *The Engineer*, published a detailed account of his design in their issue for 10 July 1863. The reduced moisture content was advantageous, requiring less time for the bricks to dry out before firing in the kiln, thus reducing production time. It used steam – drawn from the engine which powered it – to warm, plasticise and compact the wet clay during the moulding process thus, Longley claimed, improving both the density of the brick and the quality of the exterior finish. In many respects, however, his invention was simply a mechanised version of the manual process. Mass manufacture on a truly industrial scale was financially impractical for small brickworks.

was ideal for creating the necessary linings for the kilns and furnaces. Those linings had to be replaced at least once per year, so demand for the bricks was predictable and consistent.

At its peak in the middle of the 19th century, the estate-run brickworks was a major local source of employment, but the wages earned by the workforce were dependent on output. Daily wages were quite high for the period, but as 'common bricks' sold for only 30 shillings (£1.50) per thousand, they had to work hard for them.

As an example, the wages sheet for May 1845 shows that the total wage bill for the works was £49.18s.0d, of which nearly a quarter – £13.5s.5d.(£13.27) – went to John Meldrum, whose output for the month was 70,000 bricks, paid for at 3s.9d per thousand. These must have been special bricks, for which he earned over twice the rate paid for 'common bricks'.

To put the impact of industrialisation into perspective, the output of Bursledon Brickworks, using their Bennett & Sayer of Derby brick-making machine installed in 1897, regularly topped 30,000 bricks per day. Once they had two of these machines working, they could have produced 75,000 a day had demand required it – a phenomenal figure when compared with a month's output from the most productive employees at Charlestown half a century earlier.

James McGruthan earned a total of £11.1s.10d at Charlestown in May 1845, but for that he worked five and a half days on a daily rate, the remainder being paid at

right: A clay-encrusted Bennett & Sayer brickmaking machine displayed at Bursledon Brickworks in Hampshire. This machine formerly operated in Bursledon's North Works, and was moved to the museum in the South Works when the north site was demolished.

below: A collection of bricks displayed at Bursledon. Those embossed with 'BBCco' were hand-made at Burseldon, while the others have been collected from around the country.

piece-work rates. His output for the month was nearly 150,000 hand-made items of clayware – 70,000 common bricks at 1s.8d. per thousand, 63,000 drain tiles at 2s.0d. per thousand, and 12,500 pantiles at 1s.6d. per thousand.

That last figure is interesting, as until the late 18th century, the majority of pantiles used to roof buildings on the east coast of Scotland were imported from Holland and Belgium as ballast on returning coal ships.

From the wages slip, it seems that labourers or apprentices earned a mere 6d. or 8d. per day, while another McGruthen, Alan – who must have been a foreman or manager – was paid 4s.2d. a day.

19th century Charlestown must have mirrored the industrial development of Victorian Britain in microcosm. As well as the brick and tile works, the villagers could find employment on the estate itself, on the busy harbour exporting coal and lime, or in the rather less healthy conditions of the limekilns or the iron foundry, as well as the many other small support industries.

By the 1820s, with industrial development across Britain increasing in pace, demand for bricks quickly outstripped the production capacity of these

above: The patented brick-drying sheds at Bursledon were heated by recycled heat directed from the adjacent kilns, thus considerably reducing the drying time and speeding up the whole production cycle. The bricks were carefully stacked with no more than sixteen bricks in a tower — any more would have caused the bottom bricks in the pile to deform.

left: The restored Bennett & Sayer brick-making machine at Bursledon, showing the belt-driven drive-shaft and, to the right of the picture, the brick-cutting table. The extruded clay was cut into eight bricks at a time using a cheese-wire cutter, and they were then moved manually to the drying sheds — up to 33,000 a day from this machine alone.

above: Bursledon's brick-cutting table.

below: Bursledon has the only surviving operational steam engine by John Wood & Company of Wigan.

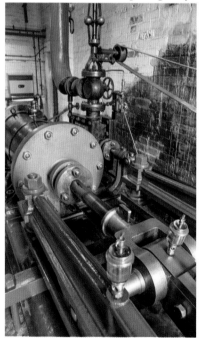

smaller brickworks, so much larger industrial production facilities had to be established. To meet this increased demand, brickmaking had to be continuous throughout the year, so large drying sheds were needed – often heated – to prepare the bricks for the kilns.

Whether they are made by hand or by machine, bricks are formed from a mixture of clay, sand, ash and a number of other optional ingredients. The precise content of the mixture determines the brick's colour, strength, and character of finish.

The Derby-built Bennett & Sayer brickmaking machine used at many large factories was engineering on a grand scale – it had to be to work with the heavy wet clay mixture. Belt drive, huge cogs and gearing transferred the power from an adjacent steam engine. In Bursledon, the necessary power came from a relatively small horizontal engine with a double-acting single cylinder, made by John Wood & Co. at their Water Heyes Foundry in Wigan in 1885.

With everyone on piece-work rates, wages were entirely dependent on the entire workforce operating in unison – from the men cutting clay, to those operating the machinery in the works.

Bursledon's clay continued to be cut by hand well into the 1930s when mechanical excavators were introduced, but as more was cut, the working face moved further and further away from the factory – eventually to a distance of more than a mile.

That was one of the factors which – along with the Health & Safety at Work Act – hastened the closure of the works in 1974.

In their heyday, brickworks worked around the clock. Much of the work was hard manual labour with newly moulded bricks being moved in wheelbarrows first to heated drying sheds, and then to the kilns for firing.

Inside Bursledon's modified Hoffman kilns – the surviving kiln block has twelve kilns in back-to-back rows of six – a system of ducts and vents ensured that the heat was dispersed evenly around the stacks of bricks before being vented out to the drying floors. The kilns were filled to the top before a crude clay and brick wall was built across the entrance. To make sure the fires were kept at the required temperature, men worked on top of the kilns, opening a number of apertures in the roof in turn and dropping fuel on to the fire and bricks below – an unpleasant and very hot job. Firing took two to three days, at temperatures up to 1100°C, and once the required temperature was reached, the workers simply stopped adding fuel, and moved on to repeat the process in the next kiln.

One kiln would be emptied each day while an adjacent kiln was being filled. The remaining ten kilns were either being heated up or cooled down in rotation. The firing system slowly built up heat in the recently filled kilns, while dampers diverted heat away from those which had been fully fired and were cooling down. Firing was a twenty-four-hour-a-day operation, with the kiln-men living on site so they were always available if needed.

Modern brickworks are highly mechanised and much less labour-intensive – and making bricks the old-fashioned way had largely been abandoned long before Burseldon closed.

The survival of any large obsolete industrial works is rare – the old facilities often being replaced with more modern ones to do the same job, and even at Bursledon, only part still exists.

The site of the north works is now occupied by the Swanwick National Air Traffic Control Centre, opened in 2002. Along with a similar facility at Prestwick in Scotland, it handles all flights over UK airspace – a far cry from a brickworks.

While bricks are still used in huge numbers, a much wider range of materials is used to build modern Britain – stone, steel, concrete, glass to name but a few, while the restoration of old buildings has led to a very welcome resurgence in demand for the traditional art of the stone-mason.

below: Part of the huge collection of clayware chimney pots displayed on the upper floor of one of Bursledon's drying sheds.

A ROOF OVER OUR HEADS

THE SKILL OF THE THATCHER is in great demand these days, in part because there are fewer of them, but also because of the continuing attraction of the thatched cottage idyll. A shortage of thatching materials in recent years – a result of poor harvests and ever more stringent rules imposed by conservationists and local authority planners – is raising the price of maintaining such a roof, but the chocolate-box cottage is losing none of its attraction.

Straw may be a lightweight material, but once the thick covering of thatch is in place, a completed roof weighs several tons, and is, in fact, much heavier than many more modern roofing materials.

During re-thatching, only rarely is all of the original straw removed. Getting a new roof usually involves raking the thatch back only as far as the first signs of robust material, so the total thickness of the roof actually recalls the history of the property. Looking under the eaves of any thatched house, several ages of straw can usually be identified, the oldest almost black but still surprisingly robust.

A well thatched roof is surprisingly durable, its longevity being dependent on several factors. The density of the straw is critical – it must be dense enough to limit water

left: A thatcher at work giving the author's house a new coat of short straw.

opposite: Leggetting – packing and dressing – a combed wheat thatch, Tivington, Somerset, 1979.

above: Thatchers often leave their 'signature' on the roof ridge. Here we have a thatched owl, top, and a pheasant, above, both seen on cottages in Wiltshire.

above right: The two owls Stan and Ollie being fixed to the new roof on the author's house.

right: The recreation of an iron-age thatched dwelling on the Hebridean island of Great Bernera. While chicken-wire holds a modern thatch in place – and keeps birds and vermin out – early thatched dwellings relied on weighted ropes, and these simple thatches often had to be completely replaced every year.

penetration, but open enough to allow the material to breath and to ensure that it dries out thoroughly after heavy rain. The pitch of the roof – much steeper than with a tiled or slated property – is critical if rain is going to run off quickly, and therefore not penetrate the straw too deeply. Hence, water continues to drip off the roof long after the rain has stopped – thatched houses have no guttering.

Thatch can trace its history back millennia, just one of many materials man has employed to roof his houses and workshops.

Thatchers have a quaint language with which to describe their materials and their array of wonderfully-named tools. The bundles of straw are usually referred to as 'nitches' – each nitch

26

Crannogs were thatched dwellings built on stilts on lakes and lochs, offering some measure of protection from attack for those who lived in them. Crannogs are believed to have been first built in Scotland and Ireland five thousand years ago, and some were still lived in until the 17th century. The site of one has been found in Llangorse Lake in the Brecon Beacons. This recreation of a crannog stands in Loch Tay, Perthshire, and is home to the Scottish Crannog Centre, offering visitors a unique glimpse of what life was like thousands of years ago.

containing 28lbs of straw. From those nitches, 'wadds' of straw are bundled, butted and bevelled before they go on the roof.

Held in place with bent hazel twigs, and packed together at a skillfully assessed density, the straw is then trimmed with a shearing hook before being combed and dressed with a 'leggett', a grooved wooden tool which helps give the job that pristine finish.

Thatchers say that old tools are much better than modern ones, and even scour antiques fairs and car boots looking for traditional tools which have stood the test of time.

Understandably, these craftsmen are very proud of their traditional skills, and usually 'sign' their roofs with a thatched bird or animal. Looking around local villages, there are pheasants, crows, squirrels and mice, and of course owls.

The durability of slate as a roofing material drove one of the great industries of the last several centuries – the remains of that industry being found across the country – in Scotland, in Cumbria and especially in Wales where entire mountains of slate were systematically mined and sold across the world.

Since the 16th century the tiny Scottish island of Easdale's history has been dominated by our appetite for roofing slates, and the fascinating scars of that industry abound.

At its peak in the mid 19th century, the quarries on this tiny island yielded over nine million slates per year – and they were in heavy demand. Along with slate from Luing, Easdale slates re-roofed the Abbey church at Iona early last century.

At first limited to surface working along the shoreline, the 16th century quarriers were migrants. They cut slates from the coastal rocks during the hours either side of low tide, and spent the rest of each day dressing them.

By the 18th century, the industry supported a considerable permanent workforce – most of the cottages on the island today were built to house them – and the slate workings had moved further from the shore, but also deeper and well below the high water level! By an ingenious system of dykes, sluices and barriers, the working day was extended to permit continuous working.

As the workings got deeper, so the problems of keeping the water at bay increased. Wind pumps were introduced early in the 19th century, and the advent of steam pumps enabled slates to be cut from faces well below the waterline.

Nine million roofing slates were exported annually from the tiny Scottish island of Easdale until the quarry workings were inundated during a storm in November 1881, leaving several deep still lagoons. The cutting equipment still lies submerged at the bottom of some of them. One lagoon now hosts the World Stone Skimming Championship, and the island's beaches are littered with scrap slate, now rounded and worn smooth by a century of tides.

Then, in November 1881, it all came to a sudden halt. A high tide breached the defences and flooded the deep workings – some over 150 feet deep – submerging steam pumps, cutting equipment and all the other paraphernalia of slate working. Two of the deep pools, unusually blue and still under the summer sun, are now the regular venue for the World Stone Skimming Championships.

The remains of the historic slate mining communities of North Wales, especially around the Portmadog and Ffestiniog area, are on the tentative list for World Heritage Site status, a protection they desperately need and richly deserve. Achieving that status is a slow process, but is expected to be confirmed in 2017 or 2018.

The former Dinorwig Quarry at Llanberis is now home to the National Slate Museum, and offers visitors a fascinating overview of the life and work of the men who cut and dressed the tens of millions of slates produced in Wales every year.

3,200 people once worked on the site – in the workshops, and high on Elidir Mountain, now itself partly hollowed out as The Electric Mountain hydro-electric power station.

The men who cut and dressed the slate, got just tuppence per slate for their labours, although the slates themselves could each sell for several pounds.

below left: The railway line which carried Dinorwig slates to the Welsh coast was built to a 4ft gauge, but all that remains of it today are these locomotive side tanks, and a collection of old wooden carriage doors.

below: Today's narrow gauge Llanberis Lake Railway still uses part of the 1845 trackbed of the slate quarry's mineral line.

Dinorwig Foundry, part of the National Slate Museum in Llanberis, North Wales. The workshops once supplied everything the quarry needed — from tools to wooden sleepers and track for the railway which carried the cut slates to the coast. The site has been left as if the workforce had just downed their tools and gone for a break.

left: Evan Wyn Thomas, a retired slate-worker, demonstrates the art of slate dressing for visitors to the National Slate Museum.

opposite page: The remains of the slate workings at Dinorwig Quarry. The slate was cut and dressed high on the ledges, with the finished slates being lowered down to the waiting railway on a steep inclined plane. The quarry once employed 3,200 people, and the men who cut the slates lived in barracks high on the mountainside.

An average of 400 slates per day was expected from each dresser – but as 28% of those slates got damaged in transit on their way to the quayside and across the world, their pay was reduced by that amount. Yes – they had to bear the cost of breakages which happened long after the perfectly cut slates had left the quarry.

But slate was not the only roofing material, and the story of one the alternatives is just as fascinating as the story of slate – albeit one initially considered to be of much lesser value than hand-cut slate.

The villages of Fife, East Lothian, and several towns right down Britain's east coast reflect the commercial acumen of

above: Detail of the pantiles on the roof of a farmhouse near Methil, Fife. Methil was once the area's major coal-exporting port.

above right: The tiled roof of a restored 18th century house on the waterfront at Dysart, Fife – one of the ports into which huge numbers of pantiles were once imported as ballast.

master-mariners and ship-owners who developed trading links with mainland Europe from the 16th century.

An empty ship is an unstable ship – mariners learned that early on in the history of seafaring, and sought ways of dealing with it. The majority of sailing ships carried loose cargo, and their vessels were ill-suited to carrying anything else on the return journey.

Coal ships exporting the produce of the Fife coalfields to the ports of northern Europe were notoriously filthy, and anything they brought back would have reflected that fact, so finding a suitable return cargo was challenging.

To avoid the risks to both ship and crew which would otherwise be a part of any return journey empty, sailing ships took on ballast to weigh the vessel down, and counter the top-heavy effect of masts and sails.

Many ships returned carrying crushed stone or sand to maintain their stability, and that ballast was dumped before they returned to port – ballast banks can still be seen off a number of Scottish ports.

Some time in the late 16th century, a merchant found an ideal return cargo. It was cheap, plentiful, and satisfied a need for a cheap roofing material. It was the humble red clay pantile.

The attractions of the pantile were numerous. Firstly, as just one step up from disposable ballast, it was cheap, and secondly it greatly speeded up the roofing process. Despite being handmade – usually the clay was pressed against a former which gave it the characteristic edge profile of an extended letter 'S' – there was a high degree of uniformity in the tile shape, and thirdly, they were relatively lightweight. This meant that they could be 'hung' on to much lighter roofing structures than would be needed to support slate or stone slabs, and because they interlocked, they gave maximum coverage for minimum weight. They could also be hung on to the same sort of roofing structure which had hitherto been used for thatch – each tile having a 'nib' which allowed it to be hung on to the cross-battens of the roof. The tiles were kept in place by their collective weight, but it was not unknown in heavy winds for a complete roof to lift off.

The pantile is still manufactured today – particularly in Yorkshire – but being machine made nowadays, it is of a more uniform shape. The curve of the 'S' is also rather lower profile today than it was three centuries ago, but the warm orange-red colour has been retained – although brown and grey tiles are also widely found in England, the Scottish preference was always for the red.

Traditionally it was a large tile, each pantile measuring 13"x9" and weighing in at five and a half pounds – it would, surely, be heresy to use metric values to describe such traditional materials.

The imported pantile was used for some major buildings – including 17th century coal tycoon Sir David Bruce's Culross Palace in Fife seen here. Most of the houses in the village of Culross, which is now maintained by the National Trust for Scotland, have pantiled roofs.

ALL MOD CONS

IN TODAY'S WORLD it is impossible to imagine what life would be like without what we think of as 'all mod cons'. But much less than 200 years ago, efficient lighting, affordable heat and fresh running water – not to mention flushing toilets – were still so far in the future that they were undreamed of by most of the population.

Perhaps because its problems were the most acute, Glasgow led the way in innovative approaches to improving and increasing its water supply – none more so than plans to turn one of the country's most beautiful lochs, Loch Katrine in the heart of the Trossachs, into the city's major reservoir. The challenge was huge, but rapidly deteriorating public health demanded something on an epic scale.

And yet the major phases of the project were completed within a very few years. Between 1853 and 1859, over 34 miles of tunnels, sluices, aqueducts and pipes were constructed.

There were objections – some experts claimed the water would be too pure to drink, while others correctly claimed that the lead in the pipes would be a health hazard.

The Admiralty sought to block the Act of Parliament, claiming it would lower the levels of the River Forth and become a hazard to naval shipping. They lost, of course, and the work went ahead.

A very discreet dam was built to raise the loch's capacity, changing its outline forever, and submerging some of its most

opposite: Hereford Waterworks' 1895-built Worth Mackenzie triple-expansion engine in steam. Demand for fresh water was such that this engine – which could pump a million gallons of fresh water in twelve hours – had to be augmented after only ten years.

Below left: Work started on the Elan Reservoirs and Aqueduct in Powys, Wales, in 1893, to supply fresh water to Birmingham. Four standard gauge railway lines – known collectively as the Elan Valley Railway – were built by Birmingham's water department to carry construction materials for the dam, aqueducts and pipeworks, and remained in use until the outbreak of the Great War. King Edward VII and Queen Alexandra officially opened the waterworks on 21 July 1904 although work on the project was not completed until late 1906. This postcard dates from the time of the opening.

Glasgow City Council's Water Committee and Water Commissioners, photographed by Thomas Annan in 1876 after inspecting the extended water works at Loch Katrine. Behind the front row, the plaque commemorates the opening of the first phase of the water system by Queen Victoria in October 1859.

below: The 'Silver Strand' on Loch Katrine, immortalised by Sir Walter Scott in his epic poem *The Lady of the Lake* was lost beneath the rising waters when the loch became a reservoir. This stereoscopic, or 3-D, photograph was taken in the late 1850s by Aberdeen photographer George Washington Wilson.

famous features. So, while accepting the need to supply water to the city, not everyone was happy at the outcome.

Significant beauty spots such as The Silver Strand, immortalized in the works of Sir Walter Scott, disappeared below the surface, to reappear only very rarely at times of drought or low rainfall – yet photographs of it continued to sell for decades afterwards.

Queen Victoria opened the first phase of the Loch Katrine scheme in 1859, and when the waters eventually reached the city in early 1860, the project was able to supply fresh water to nearly 400,000 people, some of them for the first time. Extensions in the 1870s and 1880s doubled its reach, resulting in nearly a million people in what was then one of the poorest and most overcrowded cities in Britain having one of the country's finest water supplies.

above left: Built by the Rothesay Harbour Trust in 1899 during the Bute town's hey-day as a holiday resort, the gents lavatory at the harbour is a rare Victorian survival. With ceramic faux-marble urinals and mosaic floors with the Royal Burgh's crest at the entrance, it was a source of considerable civic pride in its day.

left: Talla Waterworks was opened in 1905.

above: Tenements in Glasgow's Saltmarket, shortly before their demolition in 1866. A single pump or tap in the close served all the families who lived there, the water supplied by private companies, and often drawn directly from the polluted Clyde.

Loch Katrine still provides much of Glasgow's water, and even the steamer *Sir Walter Scott* which sails on the loch has to comply with strict guidelines to maintain its purity.

Other cities followed, and over the next century thousands of miles of pipes and tunnels were laid to feed growing populations.

On an even greater scale was Manchester's scheme to draw water from Thirlmere in the Lake District. The 96-mile long Thirlmere Aqueduct was built between 1890 and 1925 and could carry 55,000,000 gallons – 250,000 cubic metres – of water per day.

A report in the 1850s noted that there were only five water-closets in the entire city of Dundee – and three of those were in hotels! The Dundee Water Company had already built the Monikie Reservoirs to supply piped water to the city, but the majority of Dundonians were still dependent upon water carts and wells.

Edinburgh's first piped spring water had reached a select few residents as early as 1676, and the city remained largely dependent on springs until the construction of the Talla Waterworks in Peeblesshire between 1895 and 1905.

Developing Talla was every bit as big an undertaking as Glasgow's Loch Katrine project almost half a century earlier. The scheme involved the creation of the huge Talla Reservoir, more than 35 miles of pipework and numerous steam-driven pumping stations along the way. In bringing fresh water to Edinburgh, the project was beset by difficulties and disease – with numerous smallpox deaths recorded during its construction.

While cities were struggling to build reservoirs and introduce fresh water, many small towns and villages had long enjoyed pure water from wells and boreholes, and technology was soon harnessed to simplify the drawing of water from those sources. Ingenious hot air engines, and small steam engines were even installed in stately homes to bring in the modern sophistication of 'tap water' on demand – perhaps to ease the lot of the servants, but more likely to make strong statements about modernity.

For large cities – especially the largest of them all, London – the challenge was to come up with a means of reducing the

opposite & above: The two 150hp compound condensing James Watt engines at Eastney Pumping Station, Portsmouth, could pump over 2.25 million litres of sewage waste an hour. The town's sewage was stored in large tanks until the start of each ebb tide, when it was pumped out and hopefully carried well out to sea by the receding tide.

far left: This 1hp hot air engine, built by Hayward-Tyler Ltd of Luton, was installed on the Cliveden Estate in 1880 to draw water from a deep well. It is now displayed at the Hereford Waterworks Museum.

left: Also at Hereford, these twin pumping engines, built by Joseph Evans Ltd of Wolverhampton in the early 1920s, once drew well water for a school on Anglesey.

39

top: An advertisement for an early Doulton toilet.

above: This ornate late 19th century 'Oracle' toilet is in the Gladstone Pottery Museum collection.

impact of disease. A major problem in any mid 19th century city, London's was exacerbated by the fact that several of the private companies which supplied the city drew their water directly from the heavily polluted River Thames.

A series of Acts of Parliament sought to rectify the situation, starting with the Metropolis Water Act of 1852 which gave those companies three years to clean up their act. It would, however, be a further half century before full control and management of the supply and quality of water was taken over by the city fathers.

With hindsight, so much safe clean water was available by the end of the 19th century, that everyone became profligate.

There was more than enough for drinking and bathing, and as flushing toilets gained popularity, the simplest answer to the disposal of sewage was simply to flush it away – much of it into our rivers and coastal waters. It would take more than a century for the folly of such behaviour to be properly and widely recognized.

But by then rivers had additionally been compromised by a toxic cocktail of chemical outflows from factories, and many beaches were just not the places to be at low tide. Sorting all that out remains an ongoing challenge.

Left behind from the earliest attempts to tackle the challenges of both fresh water supply and sewage disposal, however, are some of the great pumping stations which were built all over the country – some to move clean water, many others to deal with effluent disposal – many of which have now been carefully restored and opened to the public for us all to enjoy.

London was one of the first cities to properly address the issue of sewage disposal, and in so doing, has left us with some of the most impressive pumping stations – cathedrals to the religion of cleanliness and hygiene – to be found anywhere in the world.

It was one thing requiring the water companies to ensure that the water they drew from the river had been 'effectually filtered' as the 1852 Act required, but quite another to remove all the infections and pathogens which the water carried – bearing in mind that the city's sewage was all sluiced back into the river.

It was in addressing that challenge that one of the greatest Victorian visionaries entered the scene – Joseph William Bazalgette, who, recommended for the post by that other great visionary Isambard Kingdom Brunel, was appointed chief engineer of the Metropolitan Board of Works in 1856.

London's sewage system – that vast underground network of brick-lined tunnels – was Bazalgette's idea, its massive scale ensuring that it has worked effectively for 150 years, and over that time has almost coped with London's mushrooming population.

While few have ever seen the inside of the sewers, many can now marvel at one of the engineering giants he designed and created – Crossness Pumping Station on the Erith Marshes. Still inside the Grade I listed building are the four original steam engines, said to be the largest surviving rotative beam engines in the world, their flywheels weighing 52 tons and their beams 47 tons.

In typical 19th century fashion, this was designed not just as a functional necessity, but as a proud and magnificent

above: This 'Niagara' toilet cistern, also from the late 19th century is on display at the Hereford Waterworks Museum.

The 'Latestas' bathroom suite, another example of richly-decorated toilet ceramics – and also displayed in the *Flushed With Pride* exhibition at the Gladstone Pottery Museum – was manufactured by Johnson Brothers in Hanley, Stoke-on-Trent, around 1891. The example was originally installed in the cloakroom off the Billiard Room at Oulton Grange Manor, Stone, Staffordshire.

statement of Victorian engineering and construction at its very best. Lofty cast iron columns and beautifully decorated arches house massive beam engines which did their job for ninety-one years, from 1865 until superseded by more powerful pumps and a new pumping station in 1956.

Another name, forever associated with matters lavatorial is that of Thomas Crapper, and it is, in a way, quite sad to realise that contrary to widely held belief, he did not invent the flushing toilet – that had been invented three centuries before him – nor did he give his name to the bodily function for which his toilets were designed – that too predated him by centuries. But with a name like that, what better occupation could there be for the young Thomas than that of a plumber, installer – and later manufacturer – of flushing toilets.

Thomas Crapper & Company were at the forefront of toilet manufacture from the early 1870s, and he did hold patents for the floating ballcock, a siphonic flush, and the shape of the U-bend.

As water became more plentiful, so did enthusiasm for flushing toilets. The company opened the country's first sanitary-ware showroom in London's King's Road, and later installed the first flushing toilets at Sandringham. The name continues today, making new bathroom equipment to Crapper's original designs.

A fascinating collection of Victorian toilets by Crapper and many others can be seen in the *Flushed with Pride* gallery at Stoke's Gladstone Pottery Museum.

While ready access to fresh water was the key to improving public health, few innovations were more important in

opposite: Fakenham Gas Works in Norfolk is one of only three preserved 'town gas' works in the United Kingdom. The others are at Carrigfergus in Northern Ireland, and Biggar in Scotland. The Fakenham works operated from 1846 until 1965. What remains, virtually intact, is a rare hand-fired retort gashouse, containing much of the original equipment. The 14 surviving retorts, however, date from the erection of a new retort house in 1910.

below: Becton Gasworks locomotive No.1, the first of a fleet of more than 25 locomotives used on the site, photographed when new in 1870. Built by Neilson & Company at their Hyde Park Works in Glasgow as job No. 1561, for the Gas Light and Coke Company, the locomotive was specially designed to operate under the gas retorts, which offered only limited headroom. It was eventually sold to the operators of the Penrhyn slate quarries in North Wales and is now preserved at Penrhyn Castle.

improving the quality of life than the introduction of coal gas for lighting, heating and cooking in the early years of the 19th century.

Before gas became widely available at the turn of a tap, lighting was of low intensity and minimal coverage, limited to candles and oil lamps, and heating to solid fuel stoves and ranges.

Coal gas, also known as 'town gas', was originally developed in 1795 purely as a means of lighting. That development of gas lighting is usually attributed to the Scottish engineer William Murdoch – who also invented the oscillating-cylinder steam engine – but it was another Scotsman, Archibald Cochrane, 9th Earl of Dundonald, who deserves that accolade, as he had first used gas for lighting his family estate in 1789.

To Murdoch, however, goes credit for the invention of the gas-holder – more usually referred to as the 'gasometer' – which was a common sight in just about every town until the introduction of North Sea gas in the 1970s.

Murdoch was, in the 1790s, employed by Boulton and Watt as an engine erector and had an enviable reputation for being able to get maximum power out of their engines for the minimum use of fuel. His experiments with gas, therefore, started out originally as a sideline, but it can be little surprise that the first commercial building to be lit by gas was Boulton & Watt's recently constructed Soho Foundry in Smethwick around 1800.

On 28 January, 1807, Pall Mall in London became the first street in the world to be lit by gas when street lights were turned on for the first time by the London and Westminster Gas Light and Coke Company.

Later known as the Gas Light and Coke Company, and formally incorporated in London in 1812 – with an address appropriately, in Pall Mall – the company became a major driver in the development of gas and coke production, with its several gasworks around the capital producing millions of cubic feet per year.

At the height of coal gas production, there were at least 1600 gasworks across Britain – some small, others massive. The three which have been preserved were all small, hand-fired operations, typical of the small-town gasworks which comprised the majority of those 1600.

The production of coal gas was a simple enough process – albeit pretty unpleasant for the workforce – and basically involved the heating of coal in an oxygen-starved atmosphere to release the gases contained within the coal. The required atmosphere was created in the retorts which were found in every gasworks – some were mechanically fed, but most small

above: This enamelled cast-iron Walsbach Kern gas fire, dating from 1890-1910, is displayed at Fakenham Gasworks Museum.

above right: Some important advice to users on the maker's plate on Ewart & Son Ltd's Victor-Geyser from 1890-1900.

below: The Station Meter at Fakenham was made by the Gas Meter Company of Wigan in 1929.

GASWORKS STREET

gasworks were hand-fed, the entire operation carried out round the clock by a surprisingly small workforce. At Fakenham, for example, there were two furnaces – known as 'producers' – one heating eight refractory retorts, the other heating six. How many were in use at any one time was dependent upon likely demand for gas, and the capacity of the gas-holder.

The coal was either shovelled by hand into the retorts sequentially – or mechanically fed into the largest retorts in city gasworks – and the retort doors sealed to create that oxygen-depleted environment. Over a period of hours, the gas was driven off and up the 'ascension pipe' and into a large 'hydraulic main' where it was given a primary wash to remove some of the tars. The water in the hydraulic main acted as a seal to prevent air mixing in with the gas when the retort doors were opened. Through a series of washers and condensers, the gas was further cooled down to the temperature of the surrounding atmosphere, that process also helping remove tars and ammonias which were drawn off into a storage tank.

A further wash eliminated everything except hydrogen sulphide, which was removed by passing the gas through filter beds of iron oxide in tanks known as 'purifiers'. The total quantity of gas produced was then measured as it passed through the station gas-meter, and pumped into the gas-holder to await demand and distribution.

above left: Sir William Armstrong's country residence at Cragside, Northumberland. It was the first house in Britain to be lit by electricity. The house had its own hydro-electric scheme installed in a new powerhouse built at Burnfoot in 1886.

The most important by-product of coal-gas manufacture was, of course, coke, which had a multitude of uses. It replaced charcoal in iron smelting furnaces, and would later prove essential in the production of the millions of tons of steel which drove Britain's industrial expansion in the 19th century. But at small gasworks, much of the coke was drawn straight from the retorts and fed into the furnaces below, providing the fuel to keep the process cycle going.

above: The 1883 Crompton Generator which produced the house's electricity. It was driven by a water-powered Gilkes turbine.

While demand for gas was still increasing, a new rival lighting system was being developed – electricity – and it would steadily replace gas as a means of lighting our streets and houses.

Gas street lighting was still commonplace in the 1950s, but within a decade most of it had been replaced first by incandescent lamps, and later by sodium. The incandescent tungsten filament lamp reigned supreme in our homes for the next sixty years before the advent of the low energy fluorescant and halide lamps we use today. Even they are likely to be phased out in the near future as LED lighting combines high output with low running costs.

GREAT PORTS & SAFE HAVENS

EVERY INDUSTRIAL INNOVATION has its time, but when that time passes and the site falls into disuse and decay, there used to be just two options – demolition and reconstruction, or abandonment. Many of the most important industrial survivals on today's heritage map are still with us because they were fortunate enough to fall into the latter category – demolishing them would have been more expensive than developing new facilities on virgin sites. A case in point is Liverpool's waterfront – as ships got bigger, they outgrew the docks which had been specially built for them, and facilities for the import and export of millions of tons of raw materials and manufactured goods moved to new docks further away from the city centre.

When ships outgrew Liverpool's Albert Dock, it was largely abandoned, and by the time of the Second World War, it was of so little commercial value that bomb damage wasn't even repaired.

The Albert Dock was the first development on the north side of the River Mersey to be designed with docks and warehousing on the same site.

Previously, warehouses had been kept separate from the loading and unloading wharfs in part because of the vested interests of the existing warehousing companies, and in part

opposite: Moored in Canning Dock, Liverpool, with the restored Grade II-listed hydraulic Pumping Station behind, the former coal-lugger *Kathleen & May* was built as the *Lizzie May* in 1900 at Connah's Quay in North Wales. She is the only surviving British-built wooden-hulled three-masted topsail schooner, and is now listed on the Historic Ships Register.

below: Stormy seas lash the breakwater at Pittenweem in Fife, while inside the harbour walls are calm waters.

left and opposite:
Jesse Hartley's
design for Liverpool's
Albert Dock set the
pattern for many
others. Built of cast
iron and brick, the
warehouses were
fireproof, with
cranes on both faces
– to lift cargo off
ships, and load
wagons on the city
side.

below left: The
701grt Mersey Pilot
Boat MV *Edmund
Gardner*, Dartmouth-
built in 1953 by
Philip & Son, is
preserved in the dry
dock at Liverpool's
Maritime Museum.

below: MV *Osterdeich*
in Manchester's No.9
Dock in 1968. As
Salford Quays, the
former docks are
now home to
residential, business,
leisure and media
facilities.

due to the construction challenges posed by nature of the reclaimed land along the river edge on which the docks were to be developed.

The idea of such an integrated dock complex had been mooted years before, but had been dismissed as impractical by those warehousing companies, citing the increased risks of fire to both vessels and warehouses.

That the Albert Dock was ever built was down to the ingenuity of Jesse Hartley, Liverpool's Dock Engineer, who solved the problem with a design which used no wood and was thus relatively fireproof. Should a fire start in either ship or warehouse, Hartley suggested, the brick and cast-iron construction he envisaged would make it relatively easy to contain. Even the roofs were to be sheet iron.

right: One of the Mersey ferries reflected in the mirror wall of the new Pierhead building as passengers disembark from the Birkenhead ferry.

below right: In the early years of the 20th century Liverpool's waterfront was a hive of activity with the quays lined with great ships. It is interesting that in this 1905 view, of the floating landing stage all the vehicles are still horse-drawn. Liverpool's maritime history is now celebrated in the Maritime Museum at the Albert Dock, and in the striking new Museum of Liverpool near the Pierhead.

His design was a refinement of the concept behind the original St Katherine's Dock in London, and, as the first fully non-combustible facility in the world, would become the blueprint for numerous other dockside warehousing complexes.

Work started in 1841 and went on twenty-four-hours a day for the first few months. Adjacent docks had to be drained, so that piling work, and the cutting of new dock entrances could take place, and the round-the-clock work schedule was intended to minimise the disruption.

The first commercial ships passed through the lock gates in 1845, and the dock was named and opened by Prince Albert in 1846.

Apart from the construction of additional warehouses in the 1850s, and the conversion of the cranes to hydraulic power, Hartley's docks remained largely unaltered for 140 years, but by the early 20th century, traffic was falling off – docks built for sailing ships were no longer well-suited to the ever-larger steamers which were plying routes between Liverpool and the rest of the world.

Finally closed in the early 1970s, the site lay derelict for a decade before work started on its remarkable restoration.

Today the Albert Dock attracts over three million visitors a year, making it the country's most visited tourist venue outside London.

Now a focal point of Liverpool's World Heritage Maritime Mercantile City – World Heritage Site status was awarded in 2004 – the docks and warehouses form the largest single group of Grade I listed buildings anywhere in the country

The 32grt steam tug *Mayflower*, seen here dwarfed by the crane on the quayside at Bristol Docks, was built by G. K. Stothert & Company in Bristol in 1861, at a cost of £1000, to work on the Sharpness and Gloucester Canal and the River Severn. Much modified over the years, she is the oldest Bristol-built ship still afloat and is said to be the oldest working tugboat in the world. Her working life was 106 years, proving her worth on several occasions – especially the harsh winter of 1962-3 when diesel tugs proved to have insufficient power to operate on the frozen canal – before finally being sold for scrap in 1967. She was saved by a group of enthusiasts with a view to restoring her in Gloucester Docks, but their efforts were beset by difficulties – including her being scuttled by vandals. In 1981 she was sold to Bristol Museums & Art Gallery and over the next six years was restored to full working order, being returned to steam in 1987. She is now regularly used to take visitors for short trips around the harbour.

Brunel's SS *Great Britain* was built in Bristol's Great Western Dock in 1843 and is now preserved there after a multi-million pound reconstruction. Of the original ship, only the hull survives.

The dock has now been fitted with a glass roof so it is possible to get a real sense of the scale of the ship's propeller and rudder. The internal reconstruction gives a vivid impression of the different classes of accommodation on a transatlantic steamship 170 years ago.

and now house numerous bars and restaurants, the Tate Liverpool, the city's Maritime Museum, The Beatles Story, hotels and numerous other attractions.

Whereas Liverpool's docks fronted on to the river, Gloucester Docks were accessed by a 16-mile canal from Sharpness reaching almost into the city centre. Work on the Gloucester and Sharpness Canal started in the 1790s, but was halted after a few years, and not restarted until Thomas Telford became Consulting Engineer, with a brief to create work for soldiers returning after 1815 from the Napoleonic Wars.

The docks were eventually opened to traffic in 1827. Further warehouse and dock complexes were added in the 1850s, and all survive largely intact.

Indeed, so much is unchanged that the docks are a popular venue for film crews seeking Victorian maritime locations, most recently in 2014 for scenes in the 2016 Disney film *Alice Through the Looking Glass* starring Johnny Depp, Anne Hathaway and Helena Bonham-Carter.

Like Liverpool's Albert Dock, the Gloucester docks and warehouses have been redeveloped for a variety of leisure and commercial uses, including a marina, the Gloucester Maritime Museum, shops and restaurants, while the dry dock is still used for the maintenance of historic ships.

above: Gloucester Docks, at the inland end of the Gloucester and Sharpness Canal. The elegant Victorian warehouses have been converted into apartments, industrial units, an antiques centre, and a host of other uses.

left: The 160grt Thames barge *Olive May* was built by Wills & Packham of Sittingbourne, Kent, in 1920, and worked until 1967 She was listed on the Historic Ships Register, but ended her life as a floating restaurant in Gloucester Docks where she sank at her moorings in 1996.

A number of ports have been so comprehensively redeveloped, that hardly a trace remains of their illustrious pasts. A particular case in point is Manchester Docks – eight of the nine docks were in fact in Salford rather than Manchester – which have now been reinvented as Salford Quays, a mix of residential, office and leisure developments.

The Port of Manchester – 32 miles from the sea – opened for business in 1894 after seven years' of digging and construction, much of it carried out by Irish 'navvies'. With many of them working with nothing more sophisticated than picks, shovels and wheelbarrows – although steam-powered mechanical diggers played a vital part – they created the Manchester Ship Canal which linked the city with the Mersey Estuary. It was estimated that it took 10,000 tons of Lancashire coal per month to feed the 173 railway

locomotives which took away the spoil, and the 180 steam engines which powered the cranes and diggers.

The original dock complex – known as Pomona Docks – was intended to comprise five separate docks, but No.5 was never built. Before the canal was even completed, three larger docks were built to meet the needs of the ever-larger ships visiting the port, they were numbered 6, 7 and 8, and the entire site was opened with much pomp and ceremony by Queen Victoria in May 1894.

No.9 Dock, the largest of them all and the last to be built, again reflected the increasing size of steamers. At over half a mile long and opened in July 1905, it was built on the site of Manchester Racecourse – which was also in Salford – and helped elevate the Port of Manchester to No.4 in the list of Britain's busiest docks.

The decline in traffic throughout the 1960s and 1970s – despite the introduction of a container terminal at the canal end of No.9 Dock – was a direct result of the decisions made when the canal was being planned a century earlier. No-one could have imagined just how big ships were destined to become. By the late 1980s, the docks and upper reaches of the canal had largely been abandoned.

opposite top: The MV *Khuzistan* unloading at Manchester's No.9 Dock in February 1968. Dock 9 was the largest, completed in the early years of the 20th century, and largely closed to traffic less than 80 years later. MV *Khuzistan* was one of many grain ships regularly visiting the dock and discharging her cargo directly into huge grain elevators at the head of the dock.

above: No.9 Dock today, redeveloped as offices and hotels.

opposite below: Apartment blocks reflected in the waters of No.8 Dock today.

above: The massive James Watt Dock at Greenock, now almost deserted, was once one of the busiest docks on the Clyde. Completed in 1886, it was built to attract transatlantic shipping to the port. The Titan 'hammerhead' cantilever crane, built by Sir William Arrol, was erected in 1917. Many of Greenock's dockside warehouses have been converted into apartments.

below: Caledonian MacBrayne's 2011-built 5,200grt MV *Finlaggan* entering the dry dock at Greenock for a routine inspection. Built not on the Clyde but at Gdansk in Poland, she operates the regular service between the Kintyre port of Kennacraig and Port Askaig on the island of Islay. The dry dock is used for maintenance work on many other vessels, including the famous paddle-steamer *Waverley*.

above: The
32,728grt *Cap
Finistère* in 2014,
leaving Portsmouth
on her regular
crossing to Bilbao in
Spain.

Their rebirth as Salford Quays has been a remarkable achievement, but sadly only a very few reminders of the glory days of the docks survived the process.

The Manchester Ship Canal was the last great canal project to be constructed in Britain, and the development of Manchester Docks arguably regenerated the city. It is, therefore, regrettable that with all the leisure developments which have taken place in Salford Quays – including the Lowry Arts Centre and the Imperial War Museum North – nowhere is the importance of this once-great port, the canal which gave access to it, and the shipping lines which used it either remembered or celebrated.

below: Tied up in
Gosport in 2014, the
sail training ship TS
Royalist, was built at
Cowes in 1971 by
Groves & Gutteridge.

Probably the best-known of Britain's historic dockyards is to be found in Portsmouth – a working ferry port and a busy naval base as well as one of the country's most popular tourist attractions. The current naval base can trace its origins back more than 800 years to the reign of King Richard I and warships were still built there well into the 20th century.

Today the Historic Dockyard is dominated by the tall masts of HMS *Warrior* at the quayside and HMS *Victory* in one of the dry docks – at the time of writing still undergoing a multi-million pound restoration.

Both are seen against a backdrop of the working naval base – often with visiting foreign warships as well as the British fleet.

right: China clay is still exported from the Cornish port of Charlestown, seen here c.1905. It is also home to several historic sailing ships used in period dramas.

below: The quayside at Bristol, photographed by Francis Frith & Co. in the late 1860s. When ships became too large for the city centre moorings, much larger docks, quays and dry docks were developed. It was in one of those dry docks that Brunel's great steamer the SS *Great Britain* was built, and today, beautifully restored, she is the city's major tourist attraction.

Across the water is Gosport, and in the deep channel between the two shores, warships and cross-channel ferries come and go throughout the day.

Around Britain's coast, many small ports, their commercial traffic gone, have now been transformed into marinas, but thanks to photography, we can still get a sense of their commercial pasts.

The early 1860s must have been an exciting time to be a photographer in the Somerset port of Watchet. The harbour was being extensively rebuilt after a fierce storm in October 1859 had caused extensive damage, sweeping away breakwaters and walls which had stood for centuries. On the outskirts of town, the West Somerset Railway – being built to Brunel's broad gauge standard – was nearing completion, and local photographer James Date, whose studio was in nearby Myrtle Street was there to capture it all.

After a number of plans had been submitted, work began on rebuilding the harbour in 1860, following designs proposed by James Abernethy. The plans for a new harbour costing £20,000 submitted by Isambard Kingdom Brunel had been rejected only weeks before Brunel's death on 1 December 1859.

Much of the harbour seen under reconstruction in Date's pictures was, itself, swept away by another great storm in 1890, just as the railway he photographed under construction was also swept away after only a few years – though that was not a storm but the replacement of Brunel's broad gauge with standard gauge in 1882.

The railway was the lifeblood of the area, and with a standard gauge mineral railway as well, running from the Brendon Hills down to the harbour, the town was a major centre for the shipping of iron ore, and for the import of timber, coal and grain.

Today Watchet harbour's main source of income is as a yacht and boat haven, and the West Somerset Railway – originally built as part of Brunel's broad-gauge Great Western Railway – survives as a tourist attraction linking the coastal towns and villages. Both are a far cry from the industrial developments which led to their construction.

Many of Date's unique photographs can be seen in Watchet's excellent Museum.

above: James Date's rare 'ambrotype' images show the rebuilding of Watchet Harbour in 1861 after an horrendous storm.

left: Watchet harbour, still a working port in 1984, is now a marina.

Falmouth in Cornwall has a much grander vision, aiming to develop its large and deep harbour – and long history of both merchant and naval shipping – into a major maritime heritage attraction.

The National Maritime Museum Cornwall opened its doors in 2003 in a specially-designed harbourside building, the result of a collaboration between the National Maritime Museum in Greenwich and the Cornwall Maritime Museum in Falmouth. While inside the boat hall, the displays are mainly sailing dinghys and yachts, the steam launch *Waterlily*, built in 1866 by J. Thornycroft & Company of Chiswick, is regularly seen doing what she was built to do.

Entrepreneurs in Falmouth have big plans to turn the port into a major centre for maritime – especially naval – heritage.

Walking around the quaysides at Edinburgh's Leith Docks, the contrast with my boyhood memories of the place is dramatic. The former Royal Yacht *Britannia*, moored in the shadow of a huge shopping centre, seems ill at ease and out of place. Two cargo vessels were tied up, but otherwise the quayside was empty.

Across one basin, acres of part-finished housing developments – some occupied, others mothballed – stand on bleak and exposed headlands where there were once warehouses and cranes.

above left: Winter storms at Lyme Regis lash over the Cobb, the curving breakwater which protects the town's harbour, featured in Jane Austen's *Persuasion* and in the film of John Fowles' novel *The French Lieutenant's Woman*.

above: The harbour in Crail, Fife, still hosts a small inshore fleet. In the harbour's seaward wall, the stones are set vertically, better to withstand the seas.

opposite: The bowsprit of the replica HMB *Endeavour*, in Falmouth Docks in 1998.

63

top: The Fife port of Methil was once thriving and busy, the major port for the shipment of coal from the Fife coalfields — 3 million tons a year at its peak — to a host of destinations around Britain and Northern Europe. The docks had been established in the middle of the 17th century specifically for that trade. Today No.3 Dock — the largest of the three docks — has been abandoned, while the remaining two continue in use. The coal trade ceased in May 1977. Nos. 1 and 2 Docks now specialise in the import and distribution of wood pulp and timber, importing 150,000 metric tonnes per year. There is also a small inshore fishing fleet.

right: Methil Docks today, without a ship in sight.

top: A postcard from the opening years of the 20th century, as sail gave way to steam, shows Leith Docks, the port for Edinburgh, in its heyday. From the mid-19th century, newspapers such as *North British Advertiser* regularly announced passenger and cargo sailings from Leith, to America, Canada, South Africa, Australia and New Zealand. There were clipper sailings to Sydney for 16 guineas, and steamer passages to Melbourne for £25 first class. Along with other shipping lines, the Leith, Hull & Hamburg Steam Packet Company sailed regularly between Leith and ports along the eastern and northern seaboard of Europe.

above left: The almost empty basin inside the breakwater at Leith Docks. Like Manchester, many of the quays and cargo areas are being redeveloped for housing, shopping and leisure.

Weeds grow through the tarmac in the car parks built to cater for the influx of holidaymakers expected to use the port's Cruise Terminal. The car parks are deserted and fenced off, not a cruise ship in sight.

As a teenager in the early 1960s, visiting Leith Docks was a holiday treat, being shown around by my great-uncle Jack Easton who had been Docks Superintendent and Chief Engineer until his retirement in 1946, the year I was born. Despite the fact that Jack had retired many years earlier, the older dockers always gave him a warm welcome, tipping their caps, and showing obvious pleasure that the old man stopped and chatted with them about past times.

The docks were then still manned by a close-knit community of men doing back-breaking work loading and

top left: Hartlepool's Maritime Experience, with HMS *Trincomalee*.

rop right: The former Humber Ferry PS *Wingfield Castle* now permanently displayed at Jackson's Dock, Hartlepool.

right: The Clyde-built *Glenlee* reflected in the frontage of Zaha Hadid's striking Riverside Museum, built on the site of the Pointhouse shipyard. Inside are many reminders of Glasgow's industrial past, including railway locomotives exported from Glasgow across the world.

unloading ships carrying loose and mixed cargoes. The quays seemed to bustle with dockers and machines as ships came and went with the tides but, even then in the early 1960s, trade was in steep decline as the port was already losing out to larger container ports elsewhere.

In the 1830s and 1840s Ellesmere Port's docks and warehouse facilities were extensively developed by Thomas Telford and William Jessop, creating an interchange between ships arriving on the River Mersey and narrowboats on the Ellesmere Canal – later amalgamated with the Shropshire Union Canal. A series of locks gave access from the docks to the canal. When a link to the Manchester Ship Canal was added, the Ship Canal siphoned much of Ellesmere Port's trade away from the docks. The upper part of the site is now home to the National Waterways Museum.

With shipping to and from the Tyne, the Clyde, Leith and many other once-great ports now much below former levels – caused, as with the demise of the Port of Manchester in the 1980s, primarily as a result of the vastly increased size and draught of cargo and container ships – Scotland's only major port is now the Grangemouth container terminal a few miles further up the Firth of Forth, but its annual throughput of freight falls far short of England's largest ports at Felixstowe, Southampton, Liverpool, Thamesport and Tilbury.

Around our coast, there are many natural harbours – large areas of calm water sheltered by the many islands which make up the British Isles. They were once key to our maritime trade – and safety.

above right: The 1780grt SS *Collindoc* was built in 1925 as the SS *D. B. Hanna*, and operated as a collier on the Great Lakes in Canada before being brought to Britain. She was mined off Southend Pier on 13 July 1941, and was towed to Scapa Flow to be sunk as a block ship in Water Sound off Burray. When this photograph of her was taken in 1972, she was surrounded by water at high tide. Today, with forty more years of sand built up around her, most of what remains is on the beach.

above: The now scant remains of the vessels seen in these 1972 views of block ships are still visible at low tide.

The logistics of moving bulk cargo in ever bigger ships has had a mixed impact on them – some have prospered, while others are now largely populated by leisure craft. But a century ago, one of those 'safe havens' turned out to be not as safe as once thought.

Scapa Flow, the biggest natural harbour in the British Isles and the second biggest in the world after Sydney Harbour, covers more than 125 square miles, sheltered by the Orkney Mainland and the islands of Hoy, Graemsay, Flotta, South Ronaldsay, Burray, Lamb Holm and Glimps Holm. Its importance in Britain's maritime history was immense.

From the 18th century, the ships of the Hudson Bay Company regularly stopped off in the Orkneys before setting off across the Atlantic. There they could take on the essential provisions for their months at sea. The impact of these regular visitors on the town of Stromness was considerable.

Not only did they take on supplies, they regularly signed up Orcadians as crew, and it is said that back in Canada in the 1790s, three-quarters of the company's workforce had come from Orkney.

In the 19th century, they were joined by the whaling fleets on their way north and growing numbers of herring boats, sometimes more than four hundred at a time. Stromness harbour itself could not cope with such a number, so at some times hundreds of boats might be anchored in Scapa Flow awaiting their turn at the quayside, or awaiting smaller tenders bringing supplies out to them. They brought with them essential work and trade for the island community.

left: The 1064grt MV *Gala* unloading at Glasson Dock, the small Lancashire port on the River Lune in 1995. The tidal rise and fall at Glasson was always a limiting factor in the operation of the docks – ships entered and left by lock gates which were only opened just before high-water, and closed again as the rising tide peaked. MV *Gala* was a regular visitor to smaller British ports from 1968 until she was broken up in 2012. Shortly after this picture was taken, she was stranded off the coast of Sweden and declared a total loss. Refloated, repaired, and renamed MV *Ala*, she continued to operate for a further seventeen years, sailing being between Methil and ports in Belgium, Sweden, Denmark and Germany.

But mention Scapa Flow to most people, and they are likely to call to mind neither the whalers nor the herring fishermen, but the British fleets in the two World Wars. To those fleets, Scapa Flow was once considered to be anything but a safe haven. It was unfortified, and while Admiral Jellicoe in the First World War felt obliged to move his fleet north from Rosyth in the Firth of Forth – the huge naval dockyard was still under construction at the time – the growing risk of U-boats called for drastic action. Old cargo ships were sunk in several of the entrances to the vast natural harbour, while others were blocked by floating anti-submarine nets. In the event, after the Battle of Jutland, the German navy rarely ventured such a great distance from its home port.

By the outbreak of World War II, those earlier defences had largely collapsed, so yet more block ships were sunk on top of the earlier ones – the remains of many of which can still be seen today. The deeper wrecks have become popular sites for visiting divers from all over the world. Some of the other entrances, or Sounds, were blocked with huge numbers of concrete blocks across which roadways were laid, and those Churchill Barriers still carry the roads which link the line of islands today.

The navy long gone, Scapa's deep water harbour is now mainly visited by tankers working in the North Sea oil industry.

below : Barry Coal Docks c.1905, as sail gave way to steam.

Arguably one of the most important safe havens ever built – as far as our twentieth-century history is concerned – was brought into service, not in British waters, but off the Normandy coast in 1944.

The largest military construction project ever undertaken – and one of the fastest – was the construction in just a few months of all the component parts for the massive Mulberry Harbours which made the liberation of France possible. Yards all along the south coast, and in the Thames Estuary, secretly built the hundreds of concrete and steel caissons and floating pontoons which would be used in the ninety days after D-Day to land the huge tonnages of men, machinery and supplies needed to support the invasion. Once constructed – using 660,000 tons of concrete and 75,000 tons of steel – the structures were sunk in the Thames Estuary and along the south coast to avoid detection until the night when they were pumped out, refloated and towed across the Channel by tugboats to Omaha and Gold Beaches.

In Nuremberg in 1946 Albert Speer, architect and mastermind of Hitler's Atlantic Wall said "To construct our defences we had in two years used some 13 million cubic metres of concrete and 1½ million tons of steel. Just two weeks after the Normandy Landings, this costly effort was brought to nothing because of an idea of simple genius. As we now know, the invasion forces brought their own harbours, and built, at Arromanches and Omaha, on unprotected coast, the necessary landing ramps."

Mulberry A, the American harbour was destroyed in a storm before it was even completed, but Mulberry B, at Arromanches, remained operational long after its ninety-day design life. An outer wall of huge concrete caissons created a breakwater, with floating landing stages inside, and mile-long floating bridges to bring supplies to shore.

After the war the floating bridges were used to replace blown up bridges across France, and some caissons were used to plug holes in Dutch dykes after a storm in 1953.

Two of the caissons can still be seen in Portland Harbour in Dorset, while other parts of the harbours were returned to Britain and can be found in coastal defences along the south-east coast of England.

opposite page: Almost a mile offshore at Arromanches in Normandy, a line of 'Phoenix' caissons, part of the 5-mile outer breakwater of Mulberry B, can still be seen. On the beach lie some of the Southampton-built floating 'Beetle' pontoons which supported the half-mile long bridges linking the floating harbour with the shore at all stages of the tide.

below: Inside one of Mulberry B's floating platforms – almost totally submerged at each high tide – the structure is still sound after seventy-two years.

THE WELCOMING LIGHT

AT TALACRE IN FLINTSHIRE, Point of Air lighthouse stands knee-deep in water when the tide is in, and in a wide expanse of rippled and ribbed sand when the tide is out. The stark red-capped white tower, and the delicate sand patterns around it left by the waves make it a popular subject for photographers. Built in 1776, this brick-built lighthouse was abandoned in 1883, and has stood redundant now for more than 130 years.

A hundred and fifty miles further north, on the beach at Southerness in Dumfriesshire, an unusual square-shaped lighthouse stands equally redundant. First built by Dumfries Town Council in 1748 – and twice increased in height – its light has not shone for eighty years. Curiously, it had no light at all for the first fifty years of its life – it was simply a marker tower to help guide sailing ships into the port of Dumfries – and a beacon was not installed until sometime around 1800. Now preserved as a tourist attraction, it is said to be the second oldest surviving lighthouse in Scotland.

The oldest lighthouse in Scotland was, ironically, built some thirty-nine years after the second oldest – but Kinnaird Head lighthouse actually had a light from its opening in 1787, at least a decade before Southerness! It is now home to the Museum of Scottish Lighthouses, and is open daily.

above: Three light bulbs provided the illumination in the Portland Bill lighthouse in the late 1980s, their effect amplified by the Fresnel lens array. Now just two halide lamps do the same job.

opposite page: The derelict, and long-redundant, Point of Air Lighthouse on the North Wales Coast, seen on a spectacularly clear late spring afternoon.

left: Southernness Lighthouse has stood idle for more than eighty years.

England's oldest lighthouse is said to be the Chalk Tower at Flamborough Head, which was first lit in 1674, although the 1st century AD Roman 'Pharos' at Dover Castle still stands, converted long ago into the bell tower for the church of St Mary de Castro.

The lighthouse is now ubiquitous across the world, albeit taking many different forms to suit changing needs and architectural styles. All are now automated, visited only occasionally for maintenance. Several are open to the public, and the long climb up into the lamp room of some of the tallest ones can be an exhilarating experience.

Britain's dangerous coastline has claimed many lives over the years, and since the closing years of the 17th century, hundreds of beacons have been built to guide ships safely to port, or to warn sailors of the perils which lie beneath the waves.

A single beacon at the end of a harbour breakwater was the simplest form of guiding light, but much more useful were pairs of lights, the relative positions of which could be triangulated to determine the exact position of the ship.

In the age of GPS and radar, we may be nearing the end of the lighthouse era, and if and when that happens, there will be some spectacular buildings awaiting a new lease of life! Some have already been converted into homes, and many of the country's surviving lightships have been removed from station and put to a variety of uses.

The real value of the lighthouse or lightship, as a beacon to guide ships into port or away from submerged rocks, has been appreciated for thousands of years, but most early lighthouses suffered from a singular problem – in bad weather, ships had to be pretty close to them before they could be seen.

In the days of small, slow-moving sailing ships, that was not really a problem – ships' captains could take immediate remedial action when they saw the beacon and avoid the treacherous rocks – but with the advent of faster and bigger sailing vessels, and even bigger steamships, the short range of the light became a real issue. The bigger the

opposite page: The lighthouse on the harbour breakwater at Newhaven on the Firth of Forth was built in 1869. Decommissioned decades ago, coloured lights now replace its original beacon.

below: Also completed in 1869, Wolf Rock Lighthouse stands 8 nautical miles off Lands End. Trinity House arranged for the SS Solva to take photographer, Robert H. Preston, out to the lighthouse in 1870. More recently, in 1977 Wolf Rock became the first lighthouse in the world to have a helipad installed on top of the lantern.

below: Portland Bill lighthouse was rebuilt in its present form in the early 20th century.

opposite page top: Lighthouses were popular subjects for Edwardian postcards. Smeaton's Tower, Plymouth was built in the mid-18th century as the third Eddystone lighthouse – on the treacherous rocks south of Plymouth Sound – to a design by John Smeaton which completely revolutionised how lighthouses were constructed. When it was replaced on Eddystone Rocks in 1882, it was dismantled and rebuilt on Plymouth Hoe as a memorial to Smeaton. This is a 1905 postcard view.

bottom: New Brighton Lighthouse – seen here in a postcard from c.1906 – was completed in 1830, to a modified 'Eddystone' design, and stands on Perch Rock. It had a range of 14 miles, and a distinctive signature of two white flashes, followed by one red. It shone for the last time in 1973. The similarities between these two towers are quite apparent.

ship, the greater the distance required before any rudder command can be successfully completed.

All too often, ships would be too close to a hazard before the beacon warned them of its location.

Much early work on increasing the effectiveness of the lighthouse revolved around improvements in the brightness of the beacon – progressing from wood fires, through combustible liquids, gases, eventually to acetylene and electricity.

Much work was also done to improve the means of projecting that light as far out to sea as possible. In the early 18th century, the 'reflector' – if such it could be called – was sometimes no more than a white-painted wall behind the beacon.

Then came silvered glass reflectors – lots of little mirrors – which collected the light and projected it out from the lighthouse. The first British lighthouses to use this system are believed to have been the Mersey lights, introduced by Liverpool Dock Master William Hutchison in 1763. By 1790, the idea of the parabolic reflector had been adopted in England and France, with the first Scottish lighthouse thus equipped being built in 1803. In all these assemblies, the reflectors were made up of static arrays which projected a wide beam of light which could be seen right across the horizon.

The first revolving light was introduced in Marstrand in Sweden in 1783, while Britain's earliest uses of this technology were probably at Flamborough Head in 1806, and

Robert Stevenson's famous Bell Rock lighthouse – now the oldest sea-washed lighthouse in the world – in 1811.

The revolving reflector – for it is the mirror and lens which rotate rather than the lamp – introduced the idea of each lighthouse having its own 'signature' in terms of frequency of flash, colour of light, and so on. Thus, sailors could tell exactly where they were by the characteristics of the beam.

In many rotating beacons, the reflector assembly floated on a pool of mercury to minimize friction and limit the amount of power needed to turn it. Health and Safety would have something to say about that if keepers were still trimming or servicing the light every day.

The earliest lighthouse to use a lens system rather than just reflectors was probably on Portland Bill in the late 1780s. It was also the first lighthouse to be fitted with the patent oil lamps designed by Swiss-born Ami Argand, who had set up in business in 1780, marketing them through a successful partnership with Matthew Boulton.

Until Thomas Rogers developed his optical system, the Portland lighthouse with its parabolic reflectors required fourteen oil lamps to produce enough light. With Rogers's lens system in place, just six Argand lamps produced a more powerful beam.

Projecting the light further and further – as required by the increasing scale and frequency of shipping – meant manufacturing bigger and bigger lenses but, of course, the bigger the lens became, the heavier it was, and the greater the energy required to rotate it.

below: Scarborough Lighthouse, c.1908, with a steam drifter tied up at the quay. Lighthouses were popular subjects for Edwardian postcards, and remain so today..

below right: Built between 1887 and 1889, Southwold Lighthouse is seen here encased in scaffolding for a major overhaul and refurbishment in summer 2015. Originally oil-fired, it was converted to electricity in 1928. Until 2012, it used three 90w lamps. Now just one 90w halide lamp suffices.

That's where the ingenuity of Augustin Fresnel (1788-1827) came in. Fresnel was an engineer by profession, but was fascinated by light – and indeed, while still in his early twenties, had put forward some radical theories about the nature of light which, in time, would prove to have been absolutely correct. But in the context of lighthouses and lightships, we remember him for what has become known as the 'Fresnel Lens' although, strictly speaking, he did not invent it!

Several optical innovators before Fresnel had deduced that the bulk of a powerful lens could be reduced by grinding the glass down to a series of concentric zones which, collectively, would produce the same optical effect as a much bigger and heavier simple lens.

The first was probably Georges-Louis Leclerc, Count Buffon in France in the first half of the 18th century, and his design was improved by, amongst others, the Scottish optical physicist David Brewster – later Sir David – in the early years of the 19th century. The essential features of Buffon's and Bewster's designs can still be seen in the general shape of lenses used in many theatrical spotlights.

left: Hartlepool's
Heugh Lighthouse, —
seen here c.1905 —
is said to have been
the first in the world
to be illuminated by
gas. It was
demolished in 1915
to make way for
wartime coastal gun
batteries, and
eventually replaced
by the tower which
is still operational
today.

Fresnel's 1822 design took the idea a step further, using a lens designed as a series of annular rings which intensified the light beam without the unwanted problem of spherical aberration, and he first applied the design to a lighthouse at Cordouan in France, at the mouth of the Gironde in the following year. That design used an array of eight Fresnel lenses and eight mirrors rotated by clockwork, and can really be seen as the first modern design of lighthouse.

Fresnel's lens array was much lighter than any previous designs, and as one of the basic features of a lighthouse is that the lens has to be able to be rotated, that reduction in weight was especially beneficial.

below left: The mirror and lens array from the Heugh lighthouse is now preserved in the Museum of Hartlepool.

below right: The much more complex lens array in Portland Bill Lighthouse, Dorset.

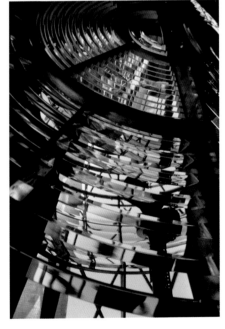

Sir David Brewster is credited with having persuaded the authorities to adopt the Fresnel lens design for use on new lighthouses then being built around Britain's treacherous coastline.

Over the following century, the idea was refined further, with Fresnel's concentric annular rings being augmented by complex assemblages of prismatic glasses to maximize the light output – often more than a hundred of them set in metal frames.

When dioptric mirrors were added to the equation by Sir James Timmins Chance in 1862, the efficiency was further improved.

Chance Brothers glasses were used in many lighthouse assemblies, as were those from the Saint Gobain company in France. For many years, thanks to the accuracy and purity of their glasses, these two manufacturers dominated the market for lighthouse optics.

Climbing up to the lamp room in a lighthouse is a revelation. The sheer scale and complexity of the lens array is remarkable – optical assemblies up to three metres in height are not uncommon – but it is, perhaps, the smallness of the light bulbs themselves which surprises most.

Between them, the mirrors and lenses of a modern lighthouse harvest every lumen of light from the lamp, sometimes projecting the beam more than 25 nautical miles – depending on the elevation of the light, and weather conditions, of course.

A lighthouse standing 300 feet above sea level, can usually be seen from a distance of more than 20 nautical miles, hence why so many are built on clifftops.

Even a wave-washed tower such as Stevenson's Bell Rock lighthouse, at just over 35 metres high, could be seen for from almost 20 miles away at sea level, and an amazing 35 miles from an elevated position on the Scottish coast.

There are now ten operational British lighthouses open to the public, all with visitor centres. Visiting them on a clear day and climbing to the top of their towers is a spectacular experience, with views stretching much further than their beacons ever project. Details and opening times for them can be found in the Gazetteer section of this book.

Several of the most famous lighthouses around Britain stand well out to sea, and to build an offshore lighthouse, solid bedrock on which to construct it and massively strong construction techniques are needed in order to ensure it can withstand the most ferocious of the seas which regularly pound Britain's coast and islands.

When there was no such firm foundation, or the waters were just too deep, another solution was required, and that was the lightship or lightvessel. The first modern lightship, designed by Robert Hamblin, was moored off the Nore sandbanks at the mouth of the Thames as early as 1732.

A tall mast initially replaced the tower of the lighthouse, with the beacon mounted on top – early examples illuminated by oil lamps – but by the very nature of the vessel and the maximum possible height of the mast or lantern tower before the ship became unstable, early lightships did not offer anything like the range of visibility afforded by taller granite or concrete lighthouse towers.

opposite top: The interior of the main hall of the Exposition Universelle in Paris in 1855, with the Saint Gobain Glass lighthouse exhibit. Lighthouse technology was developing rapidly thanks to Fresnel's innovations.

middle: Chalmers Lighthouse stands on the end of the stone pier in the Fife fishing port of Anstruther, and is seen here from a postcard c.1905. The octagonal tower was built in the early 1880s and stands 9 metres high. It is no longer lit.

bottom: The Bass Rock Lighthouse, tucked on to a ledge on the huge rock in the Firth of Forth, cost just over £8,000 to build, and the light was switched on in November 1902. From then, until it was automated and converted to electricity in 1988, the lamp was powered by paraffin gas. The beam today is produced by a high efficiency 20 watt bulb.

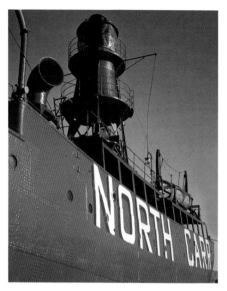

above left: The *North Carr* lightship was stationed off Fife Ness. She is now a training ship in Dundee.

above right: *LV4* was built for the Smith Knoll station off the South Wales coast, being renamed *Scarweather* when moved to the Port-Musée at Douranenez in Brittany in 1991.

right: The 1860-built *Brake*, seen here in 1935, was stationed on the Goodwins. Withdrawn in 1946 she was then used as a yacht clubhouse, but after an arson attack in 2002 she was broken up in 2011.

But for smaller slow moving vessels they were an essential navigational aid, especially around Britain's notorious sandbanks.

Two centuries of development, however, have ensured that the lightships still on station can be seen for up to 20 nautical miles.

There are eight lightships still on station around Britain's south and south-east coasts , but more than twice that number have been converted to a variety of other uses – from sailing club headquarters and restaurants to houseboats and recording studios.

Five of the decommissioned vessels have been preserved as museum ships – *LV12 Spurn Lightvessel* in Hull, *LV18 St Gowan* at Halfpenny Pier Harwich, *LV23 Mersey Bar* – now known as *Mersey Planet* – in Liverpool, *LV78 Calshot Spit* in Southampton, and *LV91 Helwick* in Swansea. Of those five, *LV 18*, *LV23* and *LV91* were all built by

Philip & Son in Dartmouth – who built many of Trinity House's vessels. *LV12* was built by the Goole Shipbuilding & Repairing Company, and *LV78* by Thornycroft in Southampton.

All of Britain's lighthouses and lightships are now automated, the lonely existence of the lighthouse keeper consigned to history.

There remains, however, something reassuring and quite special, about standing on a beach watching the lights from three or more beacons sweeping the waters.

A number of lighthouses were threatened with closure a decade ago, but reprieved after a review by Trinity House which concluded that GPS systems were not yet sufficiently accurate and reliable. A lot has happened with the technology since the 2005 review, but perhaps, even in the days of much more sophisticated GPS, mariners will resist any further attempts to switch them off for good.

above left: The Royal Sovereign lightship was stationed off Newhaven until replaced by a new lighthouse in 1971.

above: Two views of LV23 in her new role as a bar and restaurant on Liverpool's historic waterfront.

CHASING THE SILVER DARLINGS

STANDING ON THE QUAYSIDE at Newhaven harbour on the Firth of Forth as dusk falls and the lights of Granton brighten against a dramatic late autumn evening sky, it is hard to imagine that the area was once right at the heart of one of Britain's major industries. It is even harder when it is one of those magical placid nights on the river when there appears to be hardly a ripple on the water, and hardly a boat to be seen. The same description could be made of once-thriving fishing ports all around Britain's coast, many now home to nothing more than a few pleasure craft. The once-great days of the fishing industry are long gone, replaced by a few large boats, their catches now governed by rigidly policed quotas.

The fishing fleet has completely gone from Fleetwood, and from the once-great fishing port of Kingston-upon-Hull – where a century and a half of fishing is commemorated by a museum, and the restored side-trawler *Arctic Corsair*. Built in 1960 at Beverley Shipyard for the Boyd Line, *Arctic Corsair* was saved as a museum ship in 1999, and is now on the Historic Ships Register.

opposite: Fishing boats are still launched from The Stade – the Hastings Old Town beach – and hauled ashore on their return.

inset: Fishing boats and net lofts on Hastings beach – a scene from the 1890s.

below: The Hastings fleet, and the tractors, rusted by spray, which pull them on to the shingle each night. 29 boats still work from the beach, catching cod, plaice and sole.

right: In the late 1960s, both inshore and deep sea fishing fleets shared St Andrews Dock in Hull. The 725grt *Kingston Almandine* H104 was built in Aberdeen in 1950 as the *St Hubert* and was scrapped in 1975.

below: The stern trawler *Junella* H347, built by Hall Russell in Aberdeen in 1962, can be seen across the dock. *Junella* was broken up in 1992, after spending her final years in South African waters as the *Southern Ranger*.

opposite page top: Trawlers registered in Kirkcudbright, *left*, and Ballantrae, *right*, at the quayside in Kirkcudbright, south-west Scotland.

opposite middle: Fishing creels in the Scottish Fisheries Museum, Anstruther, Fife.

opposite bottom: Wick-registered WK53 *Pavonia* getting the usual welcome from the gulls off Scrabster in north-east Scotland, photographed in 1972.

Fleetwood's fishing heritage is remembered in the town's Maritime Museum, the centrepiece of which is the preserved stern trawler *Jacinta*, built at Clelands Shipbuilders in Wallsend for J. Marr & Sons of Fleetwood in 1972. Although now displayed in Fleetwood, that port was only her home for the first ten years of her working life, the vessel being transferred to Hull in 1982. In 1994 she became the top-earning British trawler, bringing in catches totalling £1.9M in

just ten months, but a year later, faced with uneconomic costs to repair her engines, she was towed to Fleetwood to become a museum ship.

Two other important preserved vessels in the history of the fishing industry are the steam drifter *Lydia Eva* YH89, based at Great Yarmouth, and the side-winder trawler *Mincarlo* now at Lowestoft Quay. *Lydia Eva* is the last surviving steam drifter in the world. All four vessels are open to the public.

A century ago, over 600,000 tons of herring alone were landed at British fishing ports each year, the majority of which were destined to be gutted, cleaned, salted or pickled, and packed in barrels by an industry which predominantly employed women – and women in their thousands. These women were following a tradition of supporting their fishermen husbands which can be traced back for centuries.

While the men caught the fish and landed them on the quayside, the majority of the work thereafter was

undertaken by a huge workforce of women, traditionally the female members of the fishermen's families, but as the herring industry grew exponentially in the closing decades of the 19th century, and was increasingly concentrated in larger centres, many of them had to adopt an itinerant lifestyle and travel and work where the fish were.

That industrialisation of the fish processing industry effectively sounded the death-knell of many smaller ports, taking away not just the work on the boats, but the women's employment in processing and selling of the fish.

In Scotland, it also created a group of almost legendary women – 'The Scotch Fisher Lassies' as Edwardian postcards invariably described them – who travelled the length of the east coast each year following the fish in search of work.

above: Unloading the catch from *Maureen* WK270 at Scrabster in 1972. Built by J. Noble of Fraserburgh in 1963, the seine-netter, later renamed *Crimson Arrow* was still working out of Girvan as a scallop dredger in 2008.

"Just now it is the herring season" wrote Alice on a postcard from North Shields on August 5th 1909, "and there are hundreds of girls from Scotland packing and curing herring, and there are large ships from every country loading

right: Berwick-on-Tweed-registered trawlers *Faithful* BK204, built in 1965, with *Sovereign* BK104 behind, tied up at the breakwater at Seahouses in Northumberland in 1974, while their crew repair nets on the quayside.

boxes and barrels of them. The girls wear boots, heavy skirts and jerseys with short sleeves. You would wonder how the boats could get in and out they are packed so close."

The girls followed the herring from Shetland right down the east coast of Scotland and England, cleaning and pickling the catches from the herring fleets as they brought ashore hundreds of thousands of tons of the 'silver darlings' each

above: Pulteney Harbour, Wick, photographed by Alexander Johnston in the 1870s — at the time the harbour was home port to over one thousand herring smacks. The number of barrels stacked on the quayside is testament to the scale of the operation.

left: Trawlers tied up at the jetty at Gairloch in north-west Scotland.

right: Steam drifters
— registered in
Kirkcaldy and North
Shields — at the
quayside in
Anstruther harbour,
Fife, c.1910.

below right: Taking
fish to market
directly from the
boats — fish porters
from Billingsgate
Market collect the
day's catch, c.1905.

below: Two 'Scotch
Fisher Lassies' pose
for an Edwardian
postcard
photographer's
camera on the
quayside at Great
Yarmouth. Many of
the girls never
returned to
Scotland, marrying
local fishermen,
raising families and
living out their lives
in the fishing ports
they had initially
arrived at as
itinerant workers.

summer and autumn. Many of the girls
came from Peterhead, first travelling
north as far as Lerwick in search of their
seasonal work, then moving south with
the work, to Fraserburgh, Peterhead,
Aberdeen, the fishing ports of the Fife
coast, then down the coasts of
Northumberland, Durham and Yorkshire,
finishing their season on the fish quays of
Grimsby and Lowestoft.

The girls slept in huts, known as 'kip
houses'. A local tradition has it that these
ramshackle dormitories were the origin
of the phrase 'having a kip', for after

above: The Southwold Sailors' Reading Room was built in 1864 as a Christian refuge for fishermen and mariners when they were not at sea. It was intended to keep them out of the pub.

top left: Four generations of Newhaven's celebrated fishwives pose for an Edwardian postcard photographer, c.1903.

above left: Marion Smith's evocative bronze sculpture *The Plough and the Reaper*, a tribute to the herring industry which once sustained the town, looks out to sea across the road from the Scottish Fisheries Museum in Anstruther, Fife. The plough in the title is the star constellation which guided mariners for centuries before GPS came along.

working very long days – sometimes as long as sixteen hours without a formal break – sleep was the only use to which they were ever likely to be put! Another explanation of the name is that as well as packing and pickling fish, smoking the herring to make kippers employed many girls, so those who did that work were often referred to as 'kipper girls'. Truth, however, is often less appealing than tradition, and 'kip-house' and 'having a kip' in fact both derive from the Norse word 'kippe' meaning a hovel – which does, of course, aptly describe their living conditions! The term 'kip-house' as applied to a humble dwelling can be traced back almost a millennium, while 'having a kip', of course, although more recent, meant being able to sleep just about anywhere.

When the herring were landed, time was of the essence, and the girls were expected to carry on working until the entire catch had been processed! There were no meal breaks,

so they were dependent upon someone bringing them some food, and there being a lull in the work so they could eat it! And when there was a longer lull – because the catch had been small, or the boats were late returning to port – they were to be seen standing around knitting while they chatted to the coopers, the fishermen and the other girls on the quayside.

But if the catch was large, it was not unusual for them to work from eight o'clock one morning until 2am or even 4am the following day! After sixteen or more hours at work, and under the low illumination offered by lanterns, the risk of cutting themselves increased considerably.

Many of the girls bound their hands with rags to reduce the risk of giving themselves serious cuts with the razor-sharp knives they used to gut the fish – and at the speed at which they worked, cuts were more likely than not even in bright sunlight! A skilled and experienced gutter could clean fifty or sixty fish per minute!

The one thing they didn't like – especially if they had recently cut themselves – was when they had to move from gutting to packing, as the salt used to preserve the fish ate into the sores on their hands! They often worked in teams of three – two gutting and cleaning, the third packing and salting, and took their turn at each activity.

above: Unloading herring at Lowestoft, 1905.

opposite page: An inshore fishing vessel moored in Loch Crinan just off the western end of John Rennie's Crinan Canal.

inset: A considerable number of small fishing ports had their own local boat repairers. Here, the Fraserburgh-registered *Providence*, FR168, is seen undergoing extensive repairs on the quayside at Eyemouth, Berwickshire, in 1973. Despite her registration, she usually worked out of Seahouses in Northumberland.

above: Before the Cod Wars, Fleetwood was a busy deep sea fishing port. These photographs were taken in 1974. The fleet has now all gone.

right: As dusk falls in February 1974, a tug-boat eases FD137 *Boston Blenheim* away from the quayside. Built by Dunston of Hessle in 1970, she had arrived in Fleetwood in January 1971 and regularly fished the waters around Iceland. Sold to Chilean owners in 1979, she was abandoned in 2013.

But fish are fickle. If the anticipated huge shoals of herring did not appear off shore at the appointed season, then there was very real hardship not just amongst the fisherfolk, but also in the many industries which depended on the success of the fishing for their own success – including the barrel-makers, sail-makers and net-makers, ship chandlers, transportation companies, and countless others.

It was said that the labours of every fishing boat which went to sea in search of either herring or white fish in those days supported the employment of up to a hundred people.

below left: From an Edwardian postcard, women working in a Peterhead kipper smokehouse. The fish-smoking industry was an essential means of preserving fish in the days before effective refrigeration and freezers, and the smokehouses of the east coast employed thousands of women. Small smokehouses can still be found dotted along the coast today.

below: Hartlepool Fish Quay in the early years of the 20th century when sail was gradually giving way to steam. Large numbers of herring drifters still relied on sail rather than steam up until the outbreak of the Great War, with new craft still being built in the early 1900s. They were cheaper to operate, albeit slower than their steam-powered counterparts. The restored sail drifter *Reaper*, based at Anstruther, is one of the last survivors.

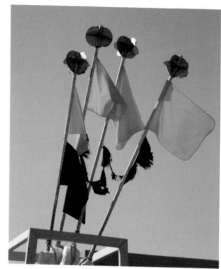

above and right:
A few boats still work off Aldeburgh's shingle beach in Suffolk — seen here in summer 2015 — and as at Hastings, they are tractor-hauled up the shingle when their day's work is over. In a number of small smokehouses along the top of the beach, visitors can buy a wide range of freshly-caught and smoked fish.

right: Edwardian fisherwomen from Southport set out their stalls on Preston Market selling freshly-caught shrimps — just a few of the million men and women who worked in the fishing industry.

If that is anywhere close to the truth, the million or so tons of mixed fish landed in Britain each year in the early 20th century, when there were about 2000 steam trawlers and at least four times that number of sailing smacks, must have supported a workforce close to one million people – or one ton of fish for every job the industry sustained.

But then fish stocks started to diminish, and many harbours lost all but the smallest of their fishing boats, as bigger vessels were concentrated in fewer ports.

For many, the great days never returned, fleet numbers dwindled and the number of people whose livelihoods were supported by the industry reduced just as dramatically. Some

left: Pittenweem
harbour in the early
1970s, a thriving
fishing port.

below: A recreation
of the interior of a
fisherman's cottage
in the Scottish
Fisheries Museum in
Anstruther.

deep sea ports bucked the trend for a time, but for most of them, the days when they sustained huge fleets of trawlers, staying at sea for weeks each trip, are gone.

With fish stocks diminishing, quotas reducing, and regulations on sustainable fishing increasing, deep sea trawling is a precarious business carried on out of just a very few ports – as the popular tv series about the lives of the trawlermen ably demonstrates.

Inshore fishing still takes place around much of Britain's coast – mainly fishing for lobster, crab, scallops and prawns and small quantities of white fish – but the lot of the inshore fisherman is, in most cases, just as challenging as his deep-sea brothers.

Fishing today is a far cry from the time when ports could boast that they were so busy that you could walk across the harbour simply by stepping from one boat to another.

THE ARMS INDUSTRY

TODAY'S SOPHISTICATED MILITARY EQUIPMENT is so expensive that very few individual companies can undertake the massive research and development necessary to bring new weapons systems to market without seeking partners.

The Typhoon fighter jet and the A400M transport plane, like so many other projects, were developed by multi-national partnerships, sharing the cost, the risks and any profits.

Less than two hundred years ago, the arms industry was very different. Military ordnance was usually developed and manufactured 'in-house' by the army and navy themselves, while the production and marketing of small arms was still almost a cottage industry when compared with the global arms trade of today.

Even fifty years ago, several world-renowned British companies still individually developed weapons systems from start to finish, but very few of them remain.

In the days long before iron hulls and steam power, Britain's great warships were nearly all built in the navy's own shipyards – Henry VIII's *Mary Rose* being the oldest survivor, now exquisitely displayed in her own custom-built museum at Portsmouth's Historic Dockyard, just a few yards from where she was originally laid down in 1510. She was launched in 1511 and towed to the Thames where she was

opposite page: The restored 9210 ton battleship HMS *Warrior* was built in 1860 at the Thames Ironworks & Shipbuilding Company at Blackwall. She was Britain's first iron-clad battleship, built at what was then the huge cost of £390,000. She could achieve a speed of 13 knots under sail, and 14.5 under steam. When under sail – all 48,400 square feet of it – her propeller could be raised out of the water to reduce drag, and her funnels could be lowered. She is now displayed at Portsmouth's Historic Dockyard.

left: Her armament comprised 26 muzzle-loading 68-pounders and 10 breech-loading 110-pounders. When she entered service she was, briefly, the largest and most powerful warship in the world.

top: One of the great 16th century bronze cannons recovered from the wreck site of the *Mary Rose*, and now displayed in the custom-built Mary Rose Museum at Portsmouth.

middle: There were three gun decks on Nelson's 2162 ton flagship HMS *Victory*. She was completed at Chatham's naval dockyard in 1765 – her keel having been laid in 1759 – so she had already been in service for forty years by the time she performed her leading role in the Battle of Trafalgar. In 1805 her armament comprised a total of 104 guns, and she had a crew of 850 men, delivering awesome firepower for her day.

bottom: Repainting HMS *Victory* during her current major restoration. How much – or how little – of the ship on which Nelson sailed still survives, no one can be entirely certain. The current project, under-pinned by almost forensic research, has involved the undoing of several earlier attempts at restoration.

above left: Musket-firing re-enacted on the quayside for visitors to the Hartlepool Maritime Experience.

above: Some of the many types of ordnance used on early 19th century warships – a far cry from the sophisticated weaponry of today.

rigged out and armed under the supervision of the Royal Armourers from the Tower of London, before entering service in 1512. Just what she looked like at that time is somewhat uncertain, as the vessel was heavily modified in 1536 to provide an additional tier of guns, raising her weight by over 40%, and increasing the number of sailors, gunners and soldiers she carried to somewhere around 700. Just nine years later, during the Battle of the Solent, she sank when overwhelmed by water while turning to fire a broadside, and remained trapped – but protected – in the silt for 446 years until raised in 1982. The process of stabilising and strengthening her timbers by replacing the sea-water first with fresh water and then with polyethylene glycol was completed in 2010. The warm air dryers were removed in early 2016 – as was the partition wall – revealing the considerable remains of the ship in all her glory.

The *Mary Rose* is a unique survival – a fact which can be put into context by remembering that there are no surviving warships from the 17th century, and only HMS *Victory* from the 18th – and what survives of the *Mary Rose* today is all original timber. That is certainly not the case with any of the other vessels in preservation.

Comparing the view of the gun-deck of HMS *Warrior* from 1860, with HMS *Victory* of a century earlier offers a vivid illustration of just how little had changed.

On land, matters were little different – it is said that the British army entered the Crimean War in 1854 still deploying

some of the heavy field artillery which had previously seen service at Waterloo.

The 1850s was a decade of major change in both the weaponry used by the British armed forces, and the procurement processes which preceded their introduction.

A significant figure in that transition was William Armstrong, later Lord Armstrong, who had already made a name for himself in the mid-1840s as an engineer – despite training as a lawyer – with his ingenious designs for water-powered hydraulic systems. These proved popular for operating everything from dockside cranes to harbour lock gates.

Britain went to war in the Crimea in 1854, and very soon reports started to be published back home – many by William Howard Russell of *The Times* – of the appalling conditions under which the troops were having to live and fight. Boggy ground, extremely wet and stormy weather, and heavy and antiquated guns all combined to slow progress.

Armstrong rose to the challenge, designing a lighter weight breech-loading field gun with a steel-lined rifled barrel encased in wrought iron, to be built at his Elswick Works on the Tyne. It fired a 5lb shell rather than a cannonball and while it proved successful in trials, the government armaments committee requested a bigger weapon, so he scaled his design up to fire an 18lb shell.

In return for passing his patent rights to the War Department, he was appointed Engineer of Rifled Ordnance

opposite page: The Artillery Camp at Balaclava during the Crimean War – a detail from one of the series of 360 photographs taken in spring and early summer 1855 by the eminent photographer Roger Fenton.

inset: The field gun assembly shop at Sir William G. Armstrong & Whitworth Limited's Elswick Works on the Tyne near Newcastle, c.1905. Armstrong had established his engineering works at Elswick in 1847, originally to build his hydraulic cranes.

below left: The giant rotating gun turrets for Dreadnought-class battleships under construction at Elswick c.1905. These massive 12" guns became the standard heavy armament on Britain's most powerful battleships. The gun and its turret weighed 46 tons, and each of the shells they fired weighed 850lb (390kg).

top: The boiler shop at the massive Vickers shipyards at Barrow-in Furness, photographed around 1910.

middle: The plate-makers' shop at Vickers, from around the same date.

bottom: As well as building ships and submarines at Barrow, Vickers produced huge tonnages of artillery and naval ordnance. This is the Shell Finishing Department, photographed just before the start of the Great War.

left: Preparing for the launch of the 19,500 ton HMS *St Vincent* at Portsmouth Dockyard in September 1908.

below: Warships being fitted out in the Devonshire Dock, Barrow-in-Furness c.1904.

at Woolwich and given a knighthood. The deal was that Armstrong's Elswick Ordnance Company would have exclusive manufacturing rights – an agreement which was short-lived as he had improved operations at Woolwich to such an extent that the guns were cheaper to make there. However, Elswick-made guns were later used in the American Civil War.

By 1864, Armstrong had merged his armaments company with his engineering business and resigned from his Woolwich post.

The company completed construction of its first warship, the ill-fated HMS *Victoria* in 1887, and in 1894, had designed and installed the steam-powered hydraulic systems in London's Tower Bridge.

top: A massive gun being manufactured at Woolwich Arsenal around 1915.

middle: Six Mark IV tanks took part in the 'Tank Banks' campaign in 1918 to sell War Bonds, raising over a hundred million pounds. The six were 113 *Julian*, seen here in Blackpool, 119 *Old Bill*, 130 *Nelson*, 137 *Drake*, 141 *Egbert* and 142 *Iron Ration*.

bottom: Another massive gun being shipped out of the Stoney Stanton Ordnance Works in Coventry c.1916. The factory had been established in 1905 under government patronage as a third large-scale arms manufacturer — the other two being Armstrong-Whitworth of Elswick and Vickers-Maxim of Barrow. The Coventry Ordnance Works Ltd was jointly owned by Clydebank shipbuilders John Brown & Company, the Govan-based Fairfield Shipbuilding & Engineering, and the Birkenhead shipbuilders Cammell-Laird. After the war, the factory became part of the newly-formed English Electric Company.

A further merger took place in 1897, when Sir W. G. Armstrong & Company merged with Manchester rival Joseph Whitworth & Company.

The combined operations of Armstrong-Whitworth proved to be a major force in British industry supplying ships and weapons throughout the Boer War and the Great War.

Many of the great guns which equipped Britain's armed forces can be seen at Fort Nelson in Hampshire, the Royal Armouries' national collection of artillery where there are over 350 big guns on display.

Fort Nelson was built on the recommendation of the 1859 Royal Commission set up by Lord Palmerston, one of five forts built to respond to a possible French attack on the Portsmouth dockyard only 5 miles away.

below left: One of the two 6-pounder guns fitted to the Mark IV tank, introduced in 1917. One of a total of 1,222 ordered by the War Department this example at Bovington was one of the 101 'male' tanks built by William Foster of Lincoln. 100 'male' tanks were also built by Armstrong-Whitworth at their Newcastle works. Metropolitan built the majority of the order — 821, including 220 'male', 421 'female' and 180 'tender' versions. William Beardmore built 25 'female' and 25 'tender', Mirlees Watson 50 'female', the remaining 100 'female' tanks coming from Coventry Ordnance Works. The 'tenders' were used as unarmed supply vehicles.

left: The gunners who operated the 6-pounders were part of a crew of eight crammed in around the massive German-designed water-cooled 6-cylinder Daimler-Benz engine which drove the 28-tonne tank. Fully fuelled and armed, the tank's small floor area would have been piled high with crates of ordnance, and with food and water for the crew.

right: 'Little Willie', built by William Foster & Co of Lincoln in late 1915, was the world's first experimental tank. It is preserved in the Tank Museum at Bovington in Dorset.

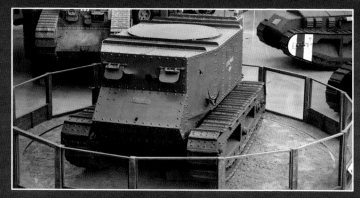

below right: This Mark II, built by Fosters in 1916, was one of the first tanks to arrive at Bovington for preservation. It took part in the battle of Arras in April 1917. For a time it was known as HMLS *Dragonfly* until *The Flying Scotsman* name was discovered under layers of old paint.

below: The world's only surviving Mark I tank — built by the Metropolitan Carriage, Wagon & Finance Company in Wednesbury in 1916 — is also at Bovington. This composite image recreates what it might have looked like approaching the German trenches on the Somme in September 1916.

In 1917, Armstrong-Whitworth was one of the engineering companies contracted to build the latest in military hardware – the Mk.IV tank – but the tank's story started well away from the Tyne.

The armoured tank was the brainchild of two men, Major Walter Wilson and William Tritton, and came into being early on in the Great War – by which time the problems of driving heavy vehicles across muddy terrain had already become only too apparent.

It is a curiosity of history that it was the Admiralty rather than the army which drove the development of the tank – through the wonderfully named Landships Committee, and with the backing of Winston Churchill. Early tanks were all known as landships, and were even named in the Admiralty tradition – HMLS *Centipede* being the first to be thus recognised.

The Landships Committee entrusted the development of the tank to Lincolnshire engineers William Foster & Company – already well-known manufacturers of heavyweight agricultural machinery.

Tracked vehicles were not entirely new, but those which were commercially available had been designed to operate over flat farmland. When faced with the undulating and deeply-pitted landscape of the battlefield, the tracks sagged

below left: Mark IV tanks were widely deployed between 1917 and the end of the war. This replica tank was built for use in Steven Spielberg's 2011 film of Michael Morpurgo's *War Horse*. It can now be seen at Bovington. The original 'B46' served with the 6th Battalion B Company, and took part in the attack on the Messines Ridge in June 1917, the first time Mark IVs had seen action.

below: The ultimate in quality personal protection – a 1920 Rolls Royce armoured field car, once used by the Royal Tank Corps.

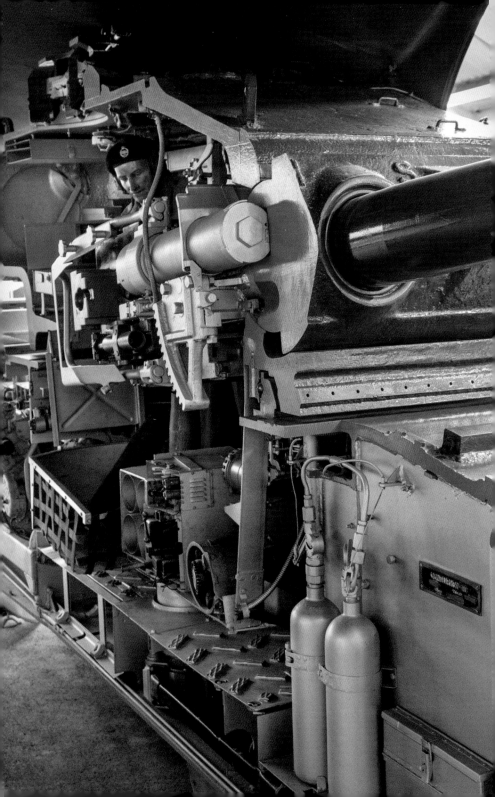

opposite page & left: The Centurion tank was designed by Vickers Armstrong, the first being completed just before the end of the Second World War. This tank was built at the Royal Ordnance Factory in Leeds as a Mk.2, but was repeatedly modified during its active service, ending up as a Mk.5. It was restored and cut into two sections in the 1990s for display at Bovington, giving a unique view of the crew conditions inside.

below: A Chieftain Main Battle Tank in Bovington's Kuwait Arena. Designed by Leyland Motors, with manufacturing shared with Vickers and later BAe Systems, the Chieftain was in service from 1967 until 1995.

and invariably fell off. Wilson and Tritton's solution was the use of simple but extremely strong tracks made of riveted interlocking steel plates, and a novel tensioning mechanism which stopped them sagging and greatly reduced the risk of them coming adrift.

The design was tried out in 1915 on the 'No.1 Lincoln Machine' – christened *Little Willie* – and proved immediately successful. Thereafter it was simply a matter of upping the scale, to create a vehicle long enough to bridge German trenches, while at the same time being able to cope with extreme changes in terrain. That latter requirement was met by running the tracks right round the machine thus creating the iconic shape of the World War 1 battle tank.

Despite its long pedigree, Fosters was a relatively small company and unable to meet the demands of manufacturing on the scale required by the War Department, so as the first

Military exercises take place on the huge expanse of Salisbury Plain regularly throughout the year, where the latest equipment is put through its paces, and the military personnel who use it are put through theirs.

above: The Gazelle helicopter was designed by Sud Aviation in France with the British Army version being built in Somerset by Westland Aircraft for more than twenty years, production ending in 1996. It played a key role in the Falklands War, and remained in active service with the army until 2012.

main picture: Getting ready for a large-scale war games on Salisbury Plain, an impressive array of Challenger tanks and other armoured vehicles sit ready for action on the crest of a hill.

top: Tanks being prepared for action at their temporary camp on the plain.

above: Warrior Tracked Armoured Vehicles ready for action. Designed by GKN which was later absorbed by British Aerospace — now BAe Systems — the army has nearly 800 of them in service.

below: The interior of submarine *Holland 1*, built in Barrow at the Vickers Maxim Works. She entered service in 1902, was lost at sea in 1913 on her way to be scrapped, recovered in 1982, and is now displayed at Gosport.

bottom: L11 and L25 moored at Chatham just after the end of the Great War.

tanks rolled off the line in Lincoln, other companies – under Fosters' supervision – were gearing up for production.

By the time the war came to an end, the list included several long-established manufacturers who had hitherto been best known for their paddle steamers, traction engines, railway locomotives and motor cars – William Beardmore of Glasgow, Armstrong-Whitworth of Elswick, The North British Locomotive Works in Glasgow, William Marshall & Sons of Gainsborough, Kitsons of Leeds, John Fowler & Company also of Leeds, and Wolseley Motors of Birmingham to name but a few.

Beardmore was also involved in the construction of HMS *Argus*, the world's first flush-deck aircraft carrier, built to a design which would provide the safest possible flight deck on which to land ship-borne aircraft, and become a basic blueprint for future carriers.

Many in the army remained fundamentally opposed to the tank, still believing in heavy guns and cavalry. Even after hostilities ended, Major-General Sir Louis Jackson was reported

as saying that "The tank was a freak. The circumstances which called it into existence were exceptional and not likely to recur. If they do, they can be dealt with by other means."

A century of continuous development throughout the world has proved that opinion to be entirely wrong.

Although it is the designers and manufacturers of guns, tanks, aircraft and ships that we celebrate in museums, there was always a vast unsung army of workers employed behind the scenes manufacturing the ordnance for all these weapons.

While Britain was at the leading edge of the technology in many areas of military hardware, the Admiralty had only been developing submarines since the beginning of the century – and those based on a modified American design – rather later than many other countries. Britain's first submarine, *Holland 1* can be seen at Gosport.

Submarines had been considered, by many in authority, to be an underhand and distinctly 'un-British' way of waging war. However, once the decision to develop them had been taken, progress was swift – from the unreliable A-class in the early 1900s, to the much larger L-class in the closing years of the Great War.

below left & right: A-Class submarines as seen in postcards c.1904.

bottom: The 580 ton HMS *M33* built in 1915, photographed in Portsmouth Historic Dockyard in 2014, with HMS *Victory* under restoration. Renamed HMS *Minerva* in 1925, *M33* is the only surviving M29-class monitor.

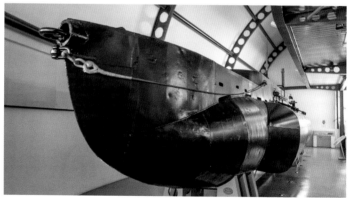

above: HMS *Alliance* was completed in 1947 by Vickers in Barrow.

above right: The periscopes on HMS *Alliance*.

right: HMS *X-24* at Gosport, one of only two surviving World War 2 midget submarines. The other, the 1944-built HMS *XE-8*, later known as *Expunger*, is preserved at Chatham after being raised from the seabed in 1973.

Britain's first submarines were all built at Barrow by Vickers, a tradition continued there today under the BAe Systems name.

There are no First World War British submarines in preservation, although the conning tower of E-17, built in just two months at Barrow in 1915 is preserved at Gosport.

From World War 2, the XE-class midget submarine HMS *XE-8* and the X-class HMS *X-24* survive. *X-24* attacked the Laksevåg floating dock at Bergen twice – in April and September 1944 –

destroying it on the second attempt. *XE-8,* built in Huddersfield by Thomas Broadbent & Sons, was deployed towards the end of the war, cutting underwater communications cables linking Japan with Singapore, Saigon and Hong Kong. *X-24* was built in 1943 by Marshall, Sons and Co. Ltd at Gainsborough and is also displayed at Gosport. Others were built at Portsmouth Dockyard, Vickers, and Varley Marine.

There are actually the same number of German midget submarines preserved in Britain today as British ones – *Biber 90* at the Imperial War Museum, and *Biber 105* at Gosport – and while no large British submarines survive from the conflict, the German submarine *U-534,* now cut into sections to reveal her interior, is preserved, somewhat incongruously, at the Woodside Ferry Terminal in Birkenhead.

And when it comes to World War 1 warships, there are just three – the small 1915 monitor and Gallipoli veteran, HMS *M33* later known as HMS *Minerva,* is preserved at Portsmouth. The 1918-built HMS *Saxifrage* – later re-named HMS *President* and now moored on the Thames, was built by Lobnitz & Company of Renfrew, while the C-class light cruiser HMS *Caroline,* built by Cammell-Laird of Birkenhead in 1914, is now moored in Belfast.

above left: What seems to the uninitiated to be a confusion of pipes, valves and levers – the control station on the submarine HMS *Alliance.*

above: The diesel engines which powered HMS *Alliance* when she was on the surface.

The 11,553 ton HMS *Belfast*, the World War II cruiser, is now moored on the Thames. She was built by Harland & Wolff in Belfast, launched in 1938 and commissioned just prior to the outbreak of war. She took part in the sinking of the *Scharnhorst* and later also served during the Korean War. She was decommissioned in 1971 and preserved as a museum ship.

Heritage Lottery funding is currently underpinning HMS *Caroline*'s restoration and projected opening as a visitor attraction, with an ambitious target to have her ready to mark the 2016 centenary of the Battle of Jutland.

World War 2 survivors are even more scarce with just two vessels in preservation – HMS *Belfast* now moored on the Thames, and the much smaller C-class cruiser HMS *Cavalier* built by J. Samuel White & Company at East Cowes, commissioned in 1944, and now preserved at Chatham Dockyard.

Construction work started on the Acheron class submarine HMS *Alliance* in the closing months of the war, but she was not commissioned until 1947. She is now displayed at Gosport in her modified 1958 form.

Post-war vessels have fared a little better – but not without some surprisingly recent casualties. Until 2014, there were three surviving Oberon-class submarines from the 1960s. Now there are just two.

HMS *Ocelot*, built at Chatham in 1962, is now back in her home port. HMS *Otus*, built by Scott's of Greenock and also launched in 1962, is now preserved in the northern German port of Sassnitz, but Falklands War veteran HMS *Onyx*, built at Birkenhead by Cammell-Laird and latterly part of the failed Warship Preservation Trust back in the port where she was built, was towed to Roseneath on the Clyde in 2014 and broken up.

The same fate befell another Falklands veteran, the Devonport-built Rothesay-class frigate HMS *Plymouth*, the last of her class and another ship entrusted to the Warship Preservation Trust. She was towed from Birkenhead to Turkey for breaking in 2014.

Putting an historic ship on the Historic Ships Register clearly does not protect it, as can frequently be seen in the pleas for funding which are reported in the pages of heritage magazines.

Alongside HMS *Plymouth* for many years at Birkenhead, and also on the register, is the 1953-built mahogany-hulled minesweeper HMS *Bronington*, looking increasingly sorry for herself. She was famously commanded in 1976 by HRH The Prince of Wales, but since the collapse of the Warship Trust in 2007 her fate has remained uncertain, with shrubs now growing through her decking.

Another minesweeper, the glass-reinforced plastic-hulled HMS *Wilton*, is now the clubhouse for the Leigh-on-Sea Yacht Club.

The nuclear Churchill-class submarine HMS *Courageous* – launched in 1970 and decommissioned in 1992 – is preserved at Devonport, the only nuclear vessel yet in preservation in Britain.

HMS *Plymouth's* triple-barrelled mortars, photographed in 1997. The Rothesay-class Type 12 steam-turbine frigate – built in Devonport, commissioned in 1961 and decommissioned in 1988 – was the last survivor of the class. She was scrapped in 2014, despite valiant attempts to save the Falklands War veteran and restore her as a museum ship.

above: The distinctive contra-rotating propellers of the Avro Shackleton, photographed at Strathallan Airfield in the 1970s. When the collection was sold off after the museum closed in 1980, the aircraft was broken up.

above right: The tail of a Shackleton at Duxford gives a clue to the aircraft's pedigree. It was a 1951 development of the 1944 Lincoln Bomber, itself derived from the legendary wartime Lancaster.

below right: A replica Airspeed Horsa AS51 Glider, unveiled in 2004 at Pegasus Bridge in Normandy sixty years after the first Horsas had landed there. Between 4000 and 5000 of these frail craft were built for the invasion — no precise records survive — the first 695 being built at Airspeed's factory in Christchurch, Hampshire.

What gets scrapped and what gets saved is something of a lottery, involving millions of pounds, sometimes-flawed business plans and huge amounts of often misplaced faith. For every success story there are many dreams which end in expensive failure.

Big ship heritage stands at a challenging crossroads. Which way should it go – restoring and preserving that past glory and then having to meet escalating operating and maintenance costs or, using today's computer technology, creating a virtual experience, and allowing the original fabric to go the way of hundreds of others – to the breaker's yard? In March 2015, the National Maritime Trust, an independent charity, outlined a long-term plan to acquire and display

left: A sectioned Rolls-Royce Nene engine on display at the Fleet Air Arm Museum in Yeovilton. The Nene, otherwise known as the RB41, was a centrifugal compressor turbo-jet engine developed in the 1940s. It was the third jet engine design to be developed by Rolls-Royce and saw service in the Hawker Sea Hawk which first flew in 1947. The last Sea Hawk was retired by the Indian Navy in 1983.

historic vessels in Falmouth Docks – setting their sights high, and hoping to include HMS *Edinburgh*, HMS *Bristol*, or any one of the several other Royal Navy vessels tagged for disposal over the coming years.

Also on their shopping list is the 1953 Centaur-class aircraft carrier HMS *Hermes*, now known as INS *Viraat*, shortly to be sold off by the Indian Navy, and even a bid for the nuclear submarine HMS *Conqueror*. It will be fascinating to monitor this ambitious project.

Preserving aircraft in an airworthy condition is just as challenging – as the retirement of XH558, the last airworthy Vulcan bomber, sadly demonstrates. It is sad to think that the famous 'howl' as it takes off may never be heard again.

There is a lack of consistency in a policy which keeps Lancasters, Hurricanes and Spitfires airworthy as pivotal

below left: The Hawker Hunter T8 was a two-seater training aircraft used by the Royal Navy to train pilots in the intricacies of carrier landings. Beyond it stands the sleek BAC-21 used as a flying testbed in the development of Concorde. The aircraft was an evolution of the Fairey Delta II, first flown in 1953, and which was developed to explore the challenges of military supersonic flight. Only two of these beautiful aircraft were ever built, and both survive – the original Fairey Delta II, WG774 is at Cosford, and this BAC-21, WD777, is at Yeovilton.

elements of Britain's wartime heritage, but has done nothing to maintain airworthy examples of the V-bomber force – the Victors, Vulcans and Valiants – which were central to the country's defences in the 1960s and '70s and just as groundbreaking in their design.

left: A replica of the Bristol Scout D biplane. It is now suspended from the ceiling over the BAC-21 and Concorde 002 at Yeovilton, minus its fabric covering to reveal its construction. A Scout C – built by the British and Colonial Aeroplane Co Ltd in Filton, Bristol – made the first take-off from an aircraft carrier, HMS *Vindex*, on 3 November 1915 and used only 46 feet of the 64 foot flight deck to get airborne. There was, then, no provision for the aircraft to land back on the vessel.

Surely some funding to keep them flying could have been found – it would be much more fitting than just having them 'stuffed and mounted' in museums.

Maintaining aircraft in static museum condition, of course, poses many fewer problems, and Britain's numerous aircraft museums offer a broad overview of the pioneering designs produced by the country's many independent aircraft manufacturers. And of course many of them hold 'flying days' when famous aircraft can still be seen doing what they were designed to do. No V-bombers, of course.

It is remarkable how many once-great names are now represented only in museum collections – Armstrong-Siddeley, A.V.Roe, Blackburn, Bristol, De Havilland, English Electric, Fairey, Gloster, Handley-Page, Hawker, Sopwith, Supermarine and Vickers, to name just a few of the larger manufacturers. They almost all succumbed to forced mergers in the 1960s as the cost and complexity of aircraft manufacture demanded economies of scale.

But even that did not save Britain's diverse aero industry, now largely represented only by Rolls Royce, BAe Systems, Airbus and numerous small specialist equipment manufacturers.

At Rosyth Dockyard on the Firth of Forth, the huge new aircraft carrier HMS *Queen Elizabeth* is, at the time of writing, nearing completion. She dominates the dockyards which have served the Royal Navy since the First World War.

When this great new ship is commissioned depends on when its aircraft – which will, disgracefully, be American not British – finally become available.

opposite page: Ten aircraft from the 1950s to the present – including a McDonell-Douglas F4 Phantom, both a de Haviland Sea Vixen and a Vampire, a Supermarine Attacker, and two Blackburn Buccaneers – stand on the recreation of HMS *Ark Royal's* flight deck, part of the award-winning 'Carrier Experience' at Yeovilton.

inset: The replica of HMS *Ark Royal's* radar operations room in the carrier's 'Island'.

GAZETTEER

BUILDING BRITAIN

Avoncroft Museum of Historic Buildings

www.avoncroft.org.uk tel: 01527 831363 Stoke Heath, Bromsgrove, Midlands B60 4JR An eclectic collection of rescued buildings spanning centuries of British domestic and commercial architecture – everything from timber-framed buildings to the post-war asbestos prefab – all reassembled on a single site. This is the story of rural British architecture in microcosm. Check website for opening times. Admission charge.

Beer Quarry Caves

www.beerquarrycaves.co.uk tel: 01297 680282 Quarry Lane, Beer, Seaton, Devon. EX12 3AT Stone has been quarried from Beer Caves for nearly two thousand years, and the underground guided tour takes visitors back in time to the Romans, and then forward through every stage of the quarry's life until it closed in 1920. From April to September guided tours run every hour from 10:30 until 16:30. Admission charge.

Bursledon Brickworks

www.bursledonbrickworks.org.uk tel: 01489 576248 Swanwick Lane, Swanwick, Southampton, SO31 7HB A unique site, and a rare time capsule, the Victorian brickworks were never updated and when they closed, the men were still cutting and working the clay in the same manner as had their Victorian and Edwardian forefathers. The museum has practical demonstrations of brickmaking using original steam-powered machinery. Open daily. Admission charge.

Chiltern Open Air Museum

www.coam.org.uk tel: 01494 871117 Newland Park, Gorelands Lane, Chalfont St Giles, Buckinghamshire HP8 4AB A collection of rescued buildings forms the heart of the museum, including a prefab, a toll house and an early 20th century public convenience. A recreation of a thatched Iron-age round house has recently been re-thatched. Open daily from the end of March until the end of October. Admission charge.

Jackfield Tile Museum

www.ironbridge.org.uk/our-attractions/jackfield-tile-museum tel: 01952 433424 Salthouse Rd, Ironbridge, Shropshire TF8 7LJ Part of the ten-museum Ironbridge Gorge World Heritage Site, the museum is housed in the former Craven Dunnill Tile Works and contains wonderful examples of decorative tiles spanning the period 1840 to 1960, when the local tile industry was at is height. There are regular tile-making demonstrations, and the factory is still in commercial production. Open daily. Admission Charge.

BUILDING BRITAIN

Saint Fagan's National History Museum
www.museumwales.ac.uk/stfagans tel: 0300 111 2 333 Cardiff, CF5 6XB St Fagan's National History Museum is an open-air museum chronicling the historical lifestyle, culture, and architecture of the Welsh people. Over the past decades, numerous buildings – from the 12th to 20th centuries – have been rescued from demolition and re-erected on the site. Amongst them are timber-framed buildings, the gentleman's convenience from Llandrindod railway station, a post war prefab and many others. There are regular demonstrations of craft skills. Open daily. Admission free.

Somerset Brick and Tile Museum
www.swheritage.org.uk/#!brick-tile-museum/cts7 tel: 01278 426088 East Quay, Bridgwater, Somerset, TA6 4AE The museum is dedicated to one of the many labour intensive coal-based industries once found in most Somerset towns. It is centred on the last tile kiln in Bridgwater, now scheduled as a Grade II* ancient monument, and last fired in 1965. There are regular demonstrations of how bricks, tiles, terracotta plaques and other wares were made. Open Tuesday and Thursday only.

The Cornice Museum of Ornamental Plasterwork
www.lgrandisonandson.co.uk/the-museum tel: 01721 720212 Innerleithen Road, Peebles, EH45 8BA This museum is hosted by a working company of ornamental plasterers. Founded in 1886, L. Grandison & Son Ltd has worked on many important buildings. The museum houses over 2000 pieces of ornamental plasterwork spanning the centuries, and includes a plasterer's workshop from the early 1900s. Open weekdays.

The Stained Glass Museum
www.stainedglassmuseum.com tel: 01353 660347 The South Triforium, Ely Cathedral, Ely, Cambridgeshire, CB7 4DL The museum has a fascinating collection of over 125 stained glass panels covering 800 years of craftsmanship, all displayed at eye level to give a unique close-up view. There is also a collection of tools and materials related to the design and manufacture of glass, lead and stained glass windows. Open daily Monday-Saturday, Sundays pm only.

Weald & Downland Open Air Museum
www.wealddown.co.uk tel: 01243 811363 Singleton, Chichester, West Sussex, PO18 0EU A collection of more than 50 buildings, spanning more than 600 years, rescued from sites across southern England, including workers' cottages, shops, farmhouses, barns, a watermill, and even a church. The museum also offers a programme of demonstrations, including blacksmithing, milling, pole-lathe turning and scything and, occasionally, traditional building techniques such as lead working, stonemasonry, lime slaking, thatching or wattle-and-daubing. Open Wednesday, Saturday and Sunday only during January to end of February. Open daily from end February to November. Admission charge.

A ROOF OVER OUR HEADS

Easdale Island Folk Museum

www.easdalemuseum.org tel: 01852 300173 Easdale Island, Nr Oban, Argyll, PA34 4TB Easdale Island was at the heart of Scotland's slate industry, and this charming little museum tells the story of those who worked in the deep slate pits from the 17th century until the workings were inundated during a ferocious storm in 1881. The relics of the slate industry can still be found all over the small island. A regular ferry service to Easdale operates from nearby Seal Island. Open daily from early April to Mid October, 11.00am-4.00pm.

Llechwedd Slate Caverns

www.llechwedd-slate-caverns.co.uk tel: 01766 830306 Blaenau Ffestiniog, Gwynedd LL41 3NB At Llechwedd the slate was mined deep underground, leaving vast caverns, and the guided tour of the mine workings includes a trip on the steepest cable railway in Britain. On the surface, visitors can see slate being worked in the workshops, housed in an original quarry building which has been in use since 1852. Open daily. Admission charge for mine tour.

National Slate Museum

www.museumwales.ac.uk/slate tel: 0300 111 2333 Llanberis, Gwynedd, LL55 4TY Set in the Victorian workshops of Dinorwig Quarry which closed in 1969, the museum tells the story of Welsh slate against the dramatic backdrop of Elidir Mountain and its centuries of slate workings. Regular demonstrations of slate dressing and slate carving. The workshops, buildings and surrounding landscape are set out as if workmen have just put down their tools and left for home. Open daily (except Saturdays in winter). Admission free.

Scottish Crannog Centre

www.crannog.co.uk tel: 01887 830583 Kenmore, Loch Tay, Aberfeldy, Perthshire, PH15 2HY This recreation of an ancient thatched dwelling, built on stilts over the waters of Loch Tay, captures something of the living conditions thousands of years ago. It was built by the Scottish Trust for Underwater Archaeology, formed to promote the research and preservation of Scotland's underwater heritage. Open daily from 1 April to 30 October. Admission charge.

Threlkeld Quarry & Mining Museum

www.threlkeldquarryandminingmuseum.co.uk tel: 01768 779747 Threlkeld Quarry, Threlkeld, Cumbria, CA12 4TT At the heart of the Cumbrian granite and slate industries, Threlkeld Quarry Museum explores the history of both stone and slate extraction. The quarry site includes displays of vintage excavators and old quarry machinery. A 2ft gauge mineral railway provides access into the inner quarry. Open daily from Easter until the end of October. Admission charge.

ALL MOD CONS

Abbey Pumping Station
www.abbeypumpingstation.org tel: 0116 299 5111 Corporation Road, Leicester, LE4 5PX Leicester's technology museum is housed in the former sewage pumping station, and amongst the exhibits, is a wide selection of toilets. The main building on the site houses four Gimson beam engines, all restored to full working order. One or more of the engines are steamed on designated days throughout the year. Open February-October. Admission charge.

Biggar Gasworks
www.historic-scotland.gov.uk/propertyresults/propertyoverview.htm?PropID=PL_031 tel: 01899 221070 Gas Works Road, Biggar, Lanarkshire ML12 6BZ The only remaining gasworks in Scotland, the gasworks opened in 1839 and closed in 1973. Still with all its machinery in situ, the museum has operational 'steam days' when the Victorian equipment can be seen running – check website. Open June-September, 2-5pm. Admission charge.

Crossness Pumping Station
www.crossness.org.uk tel: 0208 311 3711 The Old Works, Bazalgette Road, Abbey Wood, London, SE2 9AQ The Crossness Pumping Station was built by Sir Joseph Bazalgette as part of Victorian London's main sewerage system, and opened in April 1865. The Engine House has some of Britain's finest ornamental Victorian cast ironwork and contains four of the largest rotative beam engines in the world. Open various Fridays and Sundays, April-October. Admission charge.

Cruachan Hyro-electric Power Station
www.visitcruachan.co.uk tel: 0141 6149105 Cruachan Visitor Centre, Dalmally, Argyll PA33 1AN The guided tour takes you on a journey deep inside Ben Cruachan. The hydro-electric power station and its generating hall lie one kilometer inside the mountain. At its centre is a massive cavern containing the turbines and generators. Open daily in the summer, Monday to Friday in winter. Pre-booking recommended. Admission charge.

Eastney Pumping Station
www.portsmouthmuseums.co.uk/museum-service/Eastney-Beam-Engine-House tel: 023 9282 7261 Henderson Road, Eastney, Portsmouth, Hampshire PO4 9JF An impressive Victorian building containing two James Watt beam engines and pumps restored to their original 1887 condition. The Engine House is open and in steam from 1pm to 5pm in the last complete weekend (Saturday & Sunday) in every month, except December. Admission free.

Electric Mountain
www.electricmountain.co.uk tel: 01286 870636 Llanberis, Gwynedd, LL55 4UR Dinorwig Power Station was built to 'store' electricity. At times of excess capacity, electricity is used to pump water up the mountain to storage lakes. When power is needed, that water drives six hyro-electric turbines. Tours daily from Easter to October. Admission charge.

ALL MOD CONS

Fakenham Town Gasworks

www.fakenhamgasmuseum.com tel: 01553 762151 Hempton Road, Fakenham, Norfolk NR21 7LA The gasworks produced town gas from 1846 to 1965. After closure Fakenham's gasworks was preserved and is the only one remaining in England. The collections include displays of lighting, heating, cooking and domestic equipment, gas street lamps, water heaters, cookers, stoves, fires, domestic gas lighting and gas meters. Open Thursday, Friday and Bank Holidays from May-Oct. Open Thursday mornings during winter. Admission free.

Flushed with Pride at the Gladstone Pottery Museum

www.visitstoke.co.uk tel: 01782 237777 Uttoxeter Road, Longton, Stoke-on-Trent, ST3 1PQ *Flushed with Pride* is one of the galleries within the fascinating Gladstone Pottery Museum, and lifts the lid on the history of the toilet, with many examples dating back to the earliest days of the water closet. Amongst the many pioneers, the exhibition tells the story of Thomas Crapper who introduced the ballcock. Open daily. Admission charge.

London Museum of Water & Steam

www.waterandsteam.org.uk tel: 020 8568 4757 Green Dragon Lane, Brentford, London TW8 0EN Founded in 1975 as the Kew Bridge Steam Museum, the museum tells the story of London's water supply and its man stationary water pumps are regularly in steam. Open daily. Admission charge.

Museum of Power

www.museumofpower.org.uk tel: 01621 843183 Hatfield Road, Langford, Maldon, Essex CM9 6QA The main exhibits are housed in the 1920s' steam-powered water pumping station of Southend Waterworks, and the former generator hall and boiler house. Focal point is the Lilleshall vertical triple-expansion steam engine which was returned to steam for the first time in fifty years in 2011. It was capable of pumping 7 million gallons of water a day. Open February-December. Admission charge.

National Gas Museum

www.gasmuseum.co.uk tel: 0116 250 3190 195 Aylestone Road, Leicester LE2 7QH. The Museum explores all aspects of the gas industry through an eclectic collection of objects from gas meters to gas mantles and street lights. It has been described as the most significant collection of material relating to the gas industry in Britain. Open Tuesday, Wednesday and Thursday 10.30am-3.30pm. Admission free, donation appreciated.

Nuclear Power Stations

www.edfenergy.com/energy/education/visitor-centres tel: check website EDF Energy has visitor centres at all seven of its atomic power stations Dungeness B, Hartlepool, Heysham, Hinkley Point B, Hunterston B, Sizewell B and Torness – and offers regular guided tours. All are open Monday to Friday. Admission charge – check website.

ALL MOD CONS

The Milne Electrical Collection

www.milnemuseum.org.uk tel: 01798 831370 Amberley Museum, Houghton Bridge, Amberley, Arundel, West Sussex BN18 9LT The collection, part of the Amberley Museum tell the story of electricity generation and distribution, the development of domestic electrical appliances, and battery power. Contains a fascinating reconstruction of an Electricity Board Showroom from 1935. Open daily from mid-February to end of October. Admission charge.

The Waterworks Museum Hereford

www.waterworksmuseum.org.uk tel: 01432 357236 Broomy Hill, Hereford HR4 0LJ The is housed in the Victorian water pumping station which served Hereford for 120 years. Exhibits include the oldest working triple-expansion steam pumping engine in the UK. Built by Worth Mackenzie in 1895, it could pump one million gallons every twelve hours. For a full list of engines, and steam days, visit the website. The engines are in steam the first and third Sunday of each month. Open every Tuesday but not in steam. Admission charge.

Twyford Waterworks

www.twyfordwaterworks.co.uk Hazeley Road, Twyford, Hampshire SO21 1QA tel: 01962 714716 The buildings were constructed between 1898 and 1935, and although this is still a working waterworks, it still contains much of the original equipment, including a 1914 triple expansion steam pumping engine by Hathorn Davey of Leeds. Also on site are three lime kilns, installed in 1903, which were central to Twyford's water softening system. Limited opening – check website. Admission charge.

Hereford Waterworks.

BIG PORTS AND SAFE HAVENS

Aberdeen Maritime Museum
www.aberdeencity.gov.uk/tourism_visitor_attractions/galleries_museums tel: 01224 337700 Shiprow, Aberdeen AB11 5BY The museum tells the story of the North Sea, and includes exhibitions and displays of the North Boats, the fishing industry, offshore oil industry, shipbuilding and clipper ships. Open daily. Free admission.

Barrow Dock Museum
www.dockmuseum.org.uk tel: 01229 876400 North Road, Barrow-in-Furness, Cumbria LA14 2PW Built in an historic graving dock, the museum is home to a wealth of objects and information on Barrow's shipbuilding heritage. Contains the photographic archive of the Vickers shipyard, ship models and other ephemera. Open Wednesday to Sunday 11am-4pm.

Bristol M Shed Museum
www.bristolmuseums.org.uk/m-shed tel: 0117 352 6600 Princes Wharf, Wapping Rd, Bristol, BS1 4RN Housed in a former dockside warehouse, the museum tells the story of the port of Bristol. Outside can be seen dock cranes, the 1861 steam tug *Mayflower* and a number of other reminders of the working harbour. SS *Great Britain* is a short walk away. Closed on Mondays.

Eyemouth Maritime Centre World of Boats
www.worldofboats.org tel: 018907 51020 Harbour Road, Eyemouth, Berwickshire, TD14 5SS Still evolving, this museum is housed in a recreation of an 18th century frigate alongside Eyemouth's historic harbour. The 'World of Boats' collection of nearly 400 vessels from around the world contains many of the boats from the former Exeter Maritime Museum. Brunel's 1834 drag-boat *Bertha* is currently undergoing restoration. Open daily from April to November.

Glasgow Riverside Transport Museum
www.glasgowlife.co.uk/riverside tel: 0141 287 2720 100 Pointhouse Road, Glasgow G3 8RS Built on the site of the former Pointhouse Shipyard, Glasgow's new museum contains a wealth of information on the Clyde's maritime history. Moored at the quay is the barque *Glenlee* built at the Bay Yard in Port Glasgow in 1896 and now restored. Open daily.

International Slavery Museum
www.liverpoolmuseums.org.uk/ism tel: 0151 478 4499 Albert Dock , Liverpool, L3 4AQ Sited in Liverpool's historic Albert Dock is the only museum in the world dedicated to exploring the slave trade and Liverpool's part in it. Open daily. Free admission.

Hartlepool's Maritime Experience
www.hartlepoolsmaritimeexperience.com tel: 01429 860077 Maritime Ave, Hartlepool, Cleveland TS24 0XZ Three museums on the same site – Hartlepool Maritime Museum, the 1817 Mumbai-built HMS *Trincomalee* and former Humber ferry PS *Wingfield Castle* built In Hartlepool in 1934 by William Gray & Co. Open daily. Admission charge.

BIG PORTS AND SAFE HAVENS

Merseyside Maritime Museum
www.liverpoolmuseums.org.uk/maritime tel: 0151 478 4499 Albert Dock, Liverpool
L3 4AQ The museum reflects the history of the Port of Liverpool. Extensive collection
of over 2000 ship models, mostly merchant vessels – from steamships to sailing ships,
builders models to ships in bottles. Tours of the Mersey pilot boat MV *Edmund
Gardner*. Open daily.

Museum of London Docklands
www.museumoflondon.org.uk/docklands tel: 020 7001 9844 No. 1 Warehouse,
West India Quay, Hertsmere Road, Canary Wharf, London E14 4AL The museum
tells the story of the Port of London, the river and its people, from the Romans to the
present day. Located in a Georgian warehouse. Displays include tools, artifacts,
pictures. the sugar trade, slavery, whaling and the docks in wartime.

National Maritime Museum
www.rmg.co.uk/national-maritime-museum tel. 020 8858 4422 Romney Road,
Greenwich, London SE10 9NF The National Maritime Museum, the largest maritime
museum in the world, is *the* museum for anything to do with shipping and maritime
history. Part of the 'Maritime Greenwich' UNESCO World Heritage Site. In 2011 the
new Sammy Ofer Wing was opened, the largest development in its history, including
a special exhibitions gallery and a permanent exhibition, 'Voyagers', which tells the
story of Britain and the sea. Open daily. Free admission.

National Maritime Museum Cornwall
www.nmmc.co.uk tel: 01326 313388 Discovery Quay, Falmouth, Cornwall, TR11
3QY The museum is the result of collaboration between the National Maritime
Museum, Greenwich and the former Cornwall Maritime Museum in Falmouth. The
museum's collection reflects Cornwall's maritime history over the past 150 years,
focusing on the small boats which worked the ports around the Cornish coast. The
Lookout Tower offers wonderful panoramic views of the port of Falmouth. Open
daily. Admission charge.

National Waterways Museum
www.canalrivertrust.org.uk/national-waterways-museum tel: 0151 355 5017 South
Pier Road, Ellesmere Port, Merseyside CH65 4FW This vast museum includes
Telford's dock complex built under the direction of William Jessop, steam pumping
station, warehouses filled with boats. Boat trips available. Open February to
December. Admission charge.

SeaCity Museum
www.seacitymuseum.co.uk tel: 023 8083 3007 Civic Centre, Havelock Road,
Southampton, SO14 7FY SeaCity Museum tells the story of the people of
Southampton, their fascinating lives and their connections with the sea. The port's
relationship with the SS *Titanic* is featured and the Disaster Room tells the story of
the sinking from when the ship struck the iceberg to the rescue of passengers by the
SS *Carpathia*. Open daily.

Point of Air Llighthouse.

THE WELCOMING LIGHT

Arbroath Signal Tower Museum
www.angus.gov.uk/history/museums/signaltower tel: 01241 435329 Ladyloan, Arbroath, Angus DD11 1PU This museum, in the 1813 Signal Tower, the shore station for the Bell Rock Lighthouse, explores local fishing, the lives of the lighthouse keepers, and the history of Stevenson's lighthouse. Open Tues – Sat. Admission free.

Flamborough Head Lighthouse
www.trinityhouse.co.uk/lighthouses/lighthouse_list/flamborough_head.html tel: 01262 673769 Lighthouse Road, Flamborough, Bridlington, YO15 1AR Guided tours of the lighthouse are available during the summer months, closed Fridays. There are 119 steps to the top with spectacular views. Admission charge.

Lizard Lighthouse
www.trinityhouse.co.uk/lighthouses/lighthouse_list/lizard.html tel: 01326 290202 Lizard Point, nr Helston, Cornwall, TR12 7NT The twin towers of Lizard Lighthouse mark the most southerly point of mainland Britain. The Lighthouse Engine Room and contains some early engines. Closed Fridays. Admission charge.

Longstone Lighthouse
www.trinityhouse.co.uk/lighthouses/lighthouse_list/longstone.html tel: 01665 721210 Longstone Island, Northumberland. One of the most famous lighthouses in Britain, thanks to the exploits of Grace Darling. Longstone is reached by a boat trip from Seahouses. Access depends on the weather, and at the discretion of the boatman. Admission charge.

Mersey Bar Lightship
www.merseyplanet.co.uk Canning Dock, The Strand, Liverpool, L3 4AN Now known as the Mersey Planet, the lightship was built for the Mersey Docks & Harbour Board in 1960. She was the last manned lightship on the Mersey Bar. Free admission.

Museum of Scottish Lighthouses
www.lighthousemuseum.org.uk tel: 01346 511022 Kinnaird Head, Castle Terrace, Fraserburgh, Aberdeenshire AB43 9DU Housed in one of the first lighthouses built in Scotland, the museum has a large collection artifacts covering the lives of the men and families who guarded Scotland's coastline for over 200 years. Open daily. Admission charge.

Nash Point Lighthouse
www.nashpoint.co.uk tel: 07850 047721 St.Donas, Marcross CF61 1ZH One of only two lighthouses open to the public in Wales, Nash Point overlooks the Bristol Channel. Designed by James Walker, it was first lit in 1832. It was the last manned lighthouse in Wales. Admission charge. Check website for opening times and dates.

THE WELCOMING LIGHT

Portland Bill Lighthouse

www.trinityhouse.co.uk/lighthouses/lighthouse_list/portland_bill.html tel: 01305 821050 Portland Bill, Portland, Dorset, DT5 2JT The present lighthouse was constructed in 1869. A new visitor centre was opened recently. Open all year. Admission charge.

St Catherine's Lighthouse

www.trinityhouse.co.uk/lighthouses/lighthouse_list/st_catherines.html tel: 01983 730435 Niton Undercliff, Ventnor, Isle of Wight PO38 2NT Built in 1838, the lighthouse occupies a site where there has been a lighthouse for nearly 700 years. Open year round except Fridays. Guided tours available. Admission charge.

South Stack Lighthouse

www.trinityhouse.co.uk/lighthouses/lighthouse_list/south_stack.html tel: 01407 763207 South Stack, Holyhead LL65 1YH South Stack Lighthouse is situated on the north-west tip of Wales off the coast of Holy Island, accessed by a short bridge from the mainland, reached after climbing 400 steps down the cliffs. The former lighthouse engine room is now the visitor centre. Open all year. Admission charge.

Southwold Lighthouse

www.trinityhouse.co.uk/lighthouses/lighthouse_list/southwold.html tel: 01502 724729 Stradbrook Road, Southwold, IP18 6LQ The lighthouse, in the middle of the Suffolk town, was completed in 1889. It was one of the earliest to be converted to automation – in 1938. Limited openings, check website. Guided visits available. Admission charge.

Spurn Lightship

www.hullcc.gov.uk tel: 01482 300300 Hull Marina, Hull Culture & Leisure, Castle Street, Hull HU1 1TJ Built in Goole in 1927, the lightship was on station in the Humber Estuary for almost fifty years. Limited opening in summer only. Check website. Free admission.

Start Point Lighthouse

www.trinityhouse.co.uk/lighthouses/lighthouse_list/start_point.html tel: 01803 771802 Dartmouth, Kingsbridge TQ7 2ET The lighthouse stands at the end of a rocky headland. Tours run continuously until closing at 16.00 and 17.00 in July and August. The last tour is 15 minutes before closing time. Limited opening, so check website. Admission charge.

St Gowan Lightship

Halfpenny Pier, The Quay, Harwich, Essex *LV18* was built by Philip & Son of Dartmouth in 1958, sold in 1997. The vessel was used as a pirate radio station from 1999 to 2007, restored in 2011, and is now open to the public during the summer months. Admission charge.

CHASING THE SILVER DARLINGS

Aberdeen Maritime Museum

www.aberdeencity.gov.uk/tourism_visitor_attractions/galleries_museums tel: 01224 337714 Shiprow, Aberdeen AB11 5BY The City's award-winning Maritime Museum tells the story of the North Sea, and includes exhibitions and displays of the North Boats, the fishing industry, offshore oil industry, shipbuilding and clipper ships. Open daily, free admission.

Arbroath Signal Tower Museum

www.angus.gov.uk/history/museums/signaltower tel: 01241 435329 Ladyloan, Arbroath, Angus DD11 1PU This museum, in the 1813 Signal Tower, the shore station for the Bell Rock Lighthouse, explores the history of the local fishing industry – and the 'Arbroath Smokies' which made the town famous the world over – and tells the story of Stevenson's lighthouse. Open Tuesday to Saturday. Admission free.

Arctic Corsair

www.hullcc.gov.uk/museums tel: 01482 300300 Streetlife Museum of Transport, High Street, Hull HU1 1PS The last of Hull's 'sidewinder' side-trawlers, *Arctic Corsair* was built at Beverley by Cook, Welton & Gemmell in 1960, and fished off Iceland, Greenland and Newfoundland until 1987. Now fully restored to 1960s' condition. Visitors can visit the main deck, the bridge, the radio and engine rooms, the mess-room, the galley, and the fish-rooms. Open Wednesday, Saturday, Sunday. Admission free.

Brighton Fishing Museum

www.brightonfishingmuseum.org.uk tel: 01273 723064 201 King's Rd, Brighton, BN1 1NB The museum explores the history and heritage of Brighton's fishing industry through a wealth of photographs, remarkable artifacts and restored traditional Sussex clinker fishing boats. Open daily. Free admission.

Grimsby Fishing Heritage Centre

www.nelincs.gov.uk tel: 01472 323345 Alexandra Dock, Grimsby, North East Lincolnshire, DN31 1UZ Interactive museum exploring life of 1950s' fishermen and the story of Grimsby as one of the country's major fishing ports. The trawler *Ross Tiger*, GY398, is moored at the quayside. Open Tuesday to Sunday. Admission charge.

Hastings Fishermen's Museum

www.hastingsfish.co.uk/museum.htm tel: 01424 461446 Rockanore Road, Hastings, TN34 3DW In 1956 local people concerned about preserving the maritime history of Hastings took over the old Fishermen's Church. They knocked down part of a wall and pulled inside one of the last of the luggers, the *Enterprise*. All around it are models, photos, paintings, nets, ropes and a wide variety of other fishing artifacts.

CHASING THE SILVER DARLINGS

Jacinta

www.jacinta.org.uk tel: 01253 885642 Fish Dock. Fleetwood, Lancashire, FY7 6AE As a trawler working out of Fleetwood, The 1972-built *Jacinta* became the most famous stern trawler of her generation. Now moored in the town's fish dock, she is open to visitors throughout the summer months. Admission charge

Lydia Eva

www.lydiaeva.org.uk tel: 07500 603734 Hall Quay, Great Yarmouth, Norfolk NR30 2QF The Lydia Eva & Mincarlo Trust has preserved two important fishing vessels, both of which are open to the public – the Yarmouth Steam Drifter *Lydia Eva* YH89, the last survivor of a type which was once used extensively around Britain's coasts, is based at Great Yarmouth. Free admission, donations welcome.

Mincarlo

www.lydiaeva.org.uk tel: 7927 602953 Heritage Quay, South Pier, Lowestoft, Suffolk NR33 0AP The Lowestoft Side Winder Trawler *Mincarlo* LT412 was launched in 1961 at the Brooke Marine yard and is now the last survivor of a Lowestoft-built vessel. She was sold to the Lydia Eva Trust for £1 for restoration – that work is still continuing. Open to the public. Free admission, donations welcome.

Reaper

www.scotfishmuseum.org tel: 01333 310628 St Ayles, Harbourhead, Anstruther, Fife KY10 3AB The *Reaper* was built by J. & G. Forbes of Sandhaven in 1901, and now restored, is owned by the Scottish Fisheries Museum. She spent many years working as a sailing drifter, known as a 'Fifie', and has now been rebuilt in her original sail configuration as a two-masted lugger and is usually berthed in Anstruther harbour.

Ross Tiger

www.nelincs.gov.uk tel: 01472 323345 Alexandra Dock, Grimsby, North East Lincolnshire, DN31 1UZ The last of her kind and Lincolnshire's memorial to the men and women who worked out of the Port of Grimsby, the 1956 Selby-built *Ross Tiger*, was retired in 1992 and opened as a museum ship at Alexandra Dock. Open Tuesday to Sunday. Admission charge.

Scottish Fisheries Museum

www.scotfishmuseum.org tel: 01333 310628 St Ayles, Harbourhead, Anstruther, Fife KY10 3AB The museum is housed in a group of picturesque buildings overlooking the sea, and contains a mass of information and artifacts relating to the fishing industry. There is a boatyard occupying the former site of Alexander Aitken, and then Smith & Hutton Boatbuilders, and houses a fishing boat. Galleries explore both the herring and whaling industries which once employed many thousands of people. Open daily. Admission charge.

THE ARMS INDUSTRY

Barrow Dock Museum
www.dockmuseum.org.uk tel: 01229 876400 North Road, Barrow-in-Furness, Cumbria LA14 2PW Built in an historic graving dock, the museum is home to a wealth of objects and information on Barrow's shipbuilding heritage, including the Vickers photo archive. Open Wednesday - Sunday, 11-4pm.

HMS *Belfast*
www.hmsbelfast.iwm.org.uk tel: 0207 940 6300 The Queen's Walk, London, SE1 2JH Built by Harland & Wolff of Belfast, the 11,553 ton 'Edinburgh Class' cruiser entered service in 1939. Moored in the Thames since 1971, she is open daily.

Bovington Tank Museum
www.tankmuseum.org tel: 01929 405096 Linsay Road, Bovington, Dorset BH20 6JG The world's largest collection of tanks – about 300 – includes 'Little Willie', the world's first tank, and examples of just about every other British tank produced since 1916. The collection includes the only operational German 'Tiger' tank, and tanks from around the world. Live demonstrations of tanks in action in the Kuwait Arena. Open daily. Admission charge.

Bruntingthorpe Museum
www.bruntingthorpeaviation.com tel: 0116 279 9300 Bruntingthorpe Proving Ground, Lutterworth, Leicester, LE17 5QS Bruntingthorpe Aerodrome is home to the Cold War Jet Collection including a Handley-Page Victor, a Hunter, Canberra, Comet, Lightnings, Sea Vixen, Buccaneers, Jet Provosts, a Jaguar, a Nimrod MR2, a Sea Harrier and a 2-seat Jaguar. Open on Sundays only, and on occasional Open Days. Admission charge.

Chatham Historic Dockyard
www.thedockyard.co.uk tel: 01634 823807 The Historic Dockyard, Chatham, Kent ME4 4TZ Collection includes: HMS *Cavalier* was the Royal Navy's last operational World War 2 destroyer; the 1878 steam and sail iron-framed sloop HMS *Gannet*, built at Sheerness, and renamed the TS *Mercury* in 1913. Also displayed is the 1962-built HM submarine *Ocelot*. Open February to November.

Explosion! Museum of Naval Firepower
www.explosion.org.uk tel: 023 9250 5600 Priddy's Hard Heritage Area, Gosport, Hampshire PO12 4LE Centred on the historic Grand Magazine, the museum tells the history of naval ordnance, from gunpowder in the age of sail to modern missiles. Displays of small arms, torpedoes, mines, cannon, and munitions manufacture. Open daily April to October. Open Saturday and Sunday, November to March.

Fleet Air Arm Museum
www.fleetairarm.com tel: 01935 840565 Royal Naval Air Station Yeovilton, near Ilchester, Somerset BA22 8HT The museum tells the story of 100 years of naval aviation through a large collection of aircraft, ship and plane models, weapons, medals and uniforms, paintings and documents and the unique Aircraft Carrier Experience. Open daily. Admission charge.

The arms industry was concerned with more than just weapons. Built in the aftermath of the Second World War, and in the early years of the Cold War, the bunker deep below ground at Troywood in Fife — and now open to the public as 'The Secret Bunker' — had been conceived as a radar station, one of several designed to offer some token advance warning of attack. With Leuchars airbase, and Rosyth naval dockyards close by, Troywood's role was crucial in the preservation of Britain's ability to strike back after any attack.

top: The radar tracking room, bathed in an eerie light, and filled with antiquated electronics.

middle: The Royal Observer Corp's Dundee Headquarters, recreated with equipment donated by the Home Office.

bottom: The bunker had six dormitories with 300 bunks — but more than 600 staff. With the site operational round the clock, 'hot-bunking' was the order of the day.

THE ARMS INDUSTRY

Fort Nelson
www.royalarmouries.org/visit-us/fort-nelson tel: 01329 233 734 Royal Armouries Museum, Fort Nelson, Portsdown Hill Road, Fareham, PO17 6AN This Victorian fort, built in 1859, is home to the Royal Armouries national collection of artillery. The museum traces the development of artillery from pre-gunpowder siege machines to modern-day super guns. There are over 350 big guns on display. Open daily. Free admission.

Hack Green Secret Nuclear Bunker
www.hackgreen.co.uk tel: 01270 629219 Nantwich, Cheshire. CW5 8AL One of several sites throughout Britain developed during the Cold War to offer advance early warning of nuclear attack, and protection for those in command. Hack Green's displays include a rare opportunity to see up close some of Britain's former nuclear weapons, and learn their history. Open daily. Admission charge.

Hartlepool's Maritime Experience
www.hartlepoolsmaritimeexperience.com tel: 01429 860077 Maritime Ave, Hartlepool, Cleveland TS24 0XZ Three museums on the same site – Hartlepool Maritime Museum, the 1817 Mumbai-built – and fully restored – HMS *Trincomalee*, and former Humber ferry PS *Wingfield Castle* built in Hartlepool in 1934 by William Gray & Co. The recreation of the quayside includes a chandlers shop and superb exhibitions. Open daily. Admission charge.

Hendon Royal Air Force Museum
www.rafmuseum.org.uk/london tel: 020 8205 2266 Grahame Park Way, London NW9 5LL Collection of over 100 aircraft from some very early designs through to the latest modern-day jets and military aircraft, together with exhibitions and displays of some of the museum's thousands of artifacts relating to the aircraft and the history of RAF Hendon. Open daily. Admission free.

HM Frigate *Unicorn*
www.frigateunicorn.org tel: 01382-200900 Victoria Dock, Dundee, DD1 3BP The frigate *Unicorn* was built in the Royal Dockyard at Chatham and launched in 1824. She is the last intact warship from the days of sail, one of the oldest ships in the world and Scotland's only representative of the sailing navy. In 1872 she was converted into a 'Drill Ship' and moved to Dundee where she has been ever since. Open daily. Admission charge.

Imperial War Museum
www.iwm.org.uk/visits/iwm-london tel: 020 7416 5000 Lambeth Road, London SE1 6HZ *The* military museum, set up in 1917 to collect and display material relating to the Great War, which was still being fought. Two 15inch naval guns from HMS *Ramillies* and HMS *Resolution* outside the main entrance. Vivid reminders of war. Free admission.

THE ARMS INDUSTRY

Imperial War Museum Duxford

www.iwm.org.uk/visits/iwm-duxford tel: 01223 835000 Duxford, Cambridge CB22 4QR Vast collection of aircraft past and present. The AirSpace hall tells the story of aviation in Britain and the Commonwealth, with over 30 iconic aircraft including Concorde, TSR-2 and the Spitfire on display. Regular air shows. Admission charge.

Liverpool War Museum

www.liverpoolwarmuseum.co.uk tel: 0151 227 2008 1-3 Rumford Street, Liverpool, L2 8SZ Restored Underground Operations and Map Room and Teleprinter Station from the Combined Operations Unit in Derby House which was responsible for controlling the Western Approaches in the Second World War. Today, the historic wartime bunker has been restored to its appearance at the height of the war. Open March to October. Admission Charge.

MOSI Manchester

www.mosi.org.uk tel: 0161 832 2244 Liverpool Road, Castlefield, Manchester, M3 4FP The Museum of Science & Industry is housed in five listed buildings including Liverpool Road Station, the world's first passenger station. The Air and Space Hall is in the 1876 former Lower Campfield Market Hall, and celebrates Manchester's major influence – through A. V. Roe – in both civil and military aircraft development. Exhibits include a Spitfire, and English Electric P1a, and other aircraft built in the north-west of England.

Museum of Army Flying

www.armyflying.com tel: 01264 784421 Museum of Army Flying, Middle Wallop, Stockbridge, Hampshire, SO20 8DY Over 35 fixed wing and rotary aircraft flown by the army over the years including one of the few surviving Horsa gliders from the Normandy landings in 1944. Regular flying displays. Open 10am – 6.30pm daily. Admission charge.

National Museum of Flight

www.nms.ac.uk/national-museum-of-flight tel: 0300 123 6789 East Fortune Airfield, East Lothian, EH39 5LF Part of the National Museums of Scotland, the museum has a Spitfire and Avro Vulcan XM597 in its large collection of military and civil aircraft from the Great War to the present day. The restored 1940-41 hangers, scheduled to reopen in 2016, are part of the East Fortune Airfield Scheduled Monument. Open daily. Admission charge.

Newark Air Museum

www.newarkairmuseum.org tel: 01636 707170 Drove Lane, Winthorpe, Newark, Nottinghamshire, NG24 2NY This large collection of aircraft, assembled on the airfield and in the hangars of the former RAF Winthorpe, includes a Vulcan bomber, several Meteors, and a Buccaneer, a Lightning, and a Jaguar. Open daily. Admission charge.

THE ARMS INDUSTRY

Portsmouth Historic Dockyard

www.historicdockyard.co.uk tel: 023 9283 9766   Victory Gate, H M Naval Base, Main Road, Portsmouth PO1 3QX   Vessels include Henry VIII's flagship *Mary Rose* now dryng out in her new museum, HMS *Victory*, Nelson's flagship currently undergoing a major restoration, HMS *Warrior*, the only surviving iron-hulled 1860 battleship – now completely rebuilt and offering visitors a unique chance to experience what life on a warship was like 150 years ago – and Gallipoli veteran HMS *Monitor M33 (Minerva)*, built in 1915. Open daily. Admission charge.

Royal Air Force Museum

www.rafmuseum.org.uk/cosford tel: 01902 376200   Cosford, Shifnal, Shropshire TF11 8UP   The museum has a huge collection of both civil and military aircraft from most of the great British makers – A. V. Rose, Armstrong Whitworth, English Electric, Gloster, Handley Page, Hawker Siddeley, Supermarine, and many others, including the prototype English Electric P1a which evolved into the Lightning, and one of the two surviving TSR-2 fighter-bombers. Admission free.

Royal Navy Submarine Museum

www.submarine-museum.co.uk tel: 023 9251 0354   Haslar Rd, Gosport, Hampshire PO12 2AS   The Museum has three British submarines in its collection – HMS *Alliance*, built by Vickers in Barrow, Britain's first submarine, the 1901-built *Holland I* and the World War 2 midget submarine *X24*. The 40-minute tour inside HMS *Alliance* is unmissable. Open daily. Admission charge.

Solent Sky Museum

www.solentskymuseum.org tel. 02380 635830   Albert Road South, Southampton, Hampshire, SO14 3FR The museum tells the story of aviation in the Southampton and Solent area, and includes 18 aircraft types, and tells the story of 26 aircraft companies, the largest flying boat operation in the world and the Spitfire designed at Supermarine in Southampton by R.J.Mitchell. Open Tues-Sat, and Sunday pm. Admission charge.

The Secret Bunker

www.secretbunker.co.uk tel. 01333 310301   Troywood, St Andrews, Fife KY16 8QH The Secret Bunker, 100 feet underground, acted as a command centre during the Cold War. The radar room still has some of the equipment used to track Soviet incursions into British air space. The operations room is recreation of the original 1950s' RAF Command Centre which was housed at this site. A fascinating glimpse into how Britain once sought to defend itself. Open daily. Admission charge.

THE ARMS INDUSTRY

Yorkshire Air Museum

www.yorkshireairmuseum.org tel. 01904 608595 Elvington, York, YO41 4AU A large collection spanning the history of flight from the early pioneers through both world wars and the Cold War. Included in the extensive collection are Tornados, a Victor tanker, a Spitfire, a Hurricane and a rebuilt Halifax bomber. Open daily. Admission Charge.

The Avro Vulcan was the world's first delta winged bomber in 1952. Carrying a payload of 21,000lbs, the bomber's role was enhanced with the addition of Blue Steel air-launched missiles in 1963. Only two Vulcans ever took part in live combat missions. Vulcan B.2 XM597 of 50 Squadron was one them, taking part in what was at the time the longest bombing raid ever undertaken – known as the Black Buck 6 mission against Argentinian radar sites at Stanley airfield on 3 June 1982. The bomber flew from Ascension Island to the Falklands, being refuelled by Victor tankers several times on the way. XM597 is now preserved at East Fortune airfield.

INDEX

143